Ellen,

SHARKS IN BRITISH SEAS

Richard Peirce

Richard Peirce

Published by:
Shark Cornwall, Dulverton House, Crooklets,
Bude, Cornwall, EX23 8NE.

First published: 2008

ISBN no. 978-0-9558694

Editors : Anthony Bush, Tim Davison
Illustrator : Per Larsen
Photo credits/copyrights : As on photos
Front cover photograph : Chris Fallows

Printed and bound in England by
SR Print Management Limited, 29 Empire Industrial Park,
Brickyard Road, Aldridge, Walsall, WS9 8UY.

– – – – – –

"This book is for the sharks; thank you for some of the best moments of my life."

– – – – – –

SOON TO BE PUBLISHED BY THE SAME AUTHOR.

"Shark adventures – the expeditions".
"Pocket guide to Sharks in British Seas".

OTHER PRODUCTS

"Porbeagles in Peril" - DVD remake, short film (Simon Spear - Richard Peirce)
"Sharks in British Seas" - DVD (Simon Spear - Richard Peirce)

Foreword – Richard E Grant

'Cows are statistically more dangerous to Britons than sharks' is just one of the multitude of fascinating facts to be found in these pages. But there is nothing quite like a shark story to get your pulse soaring. It's extraordinary that, having been swimming the oceans for 400 millions years, sharks have been hunted down, fished and reduced to an endangered species within our lifetime, in less than a century.

Whatever the grim statistics, no other creatures, apart from crocodiles, seem to grip our imaginations quite like sharks do. Lions in Africa seem to have grown in- ured to busloads of camera clickers. Crocs mostly seem to lie around basking in the sun. But sharks are always on the move, ready to come and get you! In my experience, a shark story is a guaranteed attention grabber – making adult listeners as wide eyed as they once were when listening to Grimm's fairy tales - satisfying our deep-seated need to be terrified, by the unseen, the unknown and the untamed.

Unlike many endangered species, these creatures don't have any cuddly, 'adopt a Great White' cosiness about them. This book seeks to present the facts alongside the fictions that have accrued into myth and legend about these 'blank eyed', apparently unknowable animals.

When I was eight-years-old on holiday in Mozambique, our motorboat engine conked out whilst we were cruising around a large lagoon. I will never forget the sight of a shark's fin breaking the surface and heading towards us. My father tried to keep us all calm, that is until the shark circled the boat and then repeatedly 'bumped' into it, rocking it from side to side. We all started screaming. Because the water was so calm and flat, our yelling was heard some distance away and another launch eventually came to our rescue.

It turned out that the Zambezi shark had been 'trapped' within the lagoon for six months when the mouth into the open sea had sanded up during high tides and, reportedly, became increasingly aggressive. This experience inspired my lifelong fascination of sharks. In retrospect, I assume the 'bumping' of our boat was simply the shark's curiosity rather than any "Spielbergian" mission to Suchi us all for it's supper.

When I was recently offered the chance to join Ruby Wax, Colin Jackson and Amy Nuttall inside a perspex 'drum' off the coast of Cape Town to see Great Whites under water and close up, I dived at it. NOTHING prepared me for the sheer exhilaration and adrenalin rush of being within 'touching' distance of these powerful animals.

The facts about sharks outstrip their fiction. If we cut Shark fin soup off the menu (rather than their backs) we could increase and restore shark populations to what they once were. What say you?

INTRODUCTION

In 2003 I wanted to buy a book on British sharks to give as a present to my friend, Craig Ferreira from South Africa, who had come to work with me on an expedition off Cornwall. I couldn't find a book in print so Craig missed out on his gift.

When chumming (laying a scent trail in the water) most of the time is spent doing very little while waiting for sharks to turn up, so there's lots of time to think and hatch plots on these expeditions. Whilst chumming in the Adriatic in 2005 my thoughts kept returning to the irony of my travelling around all over the world seeking sharks, when we have some 30 species in British waters. Many become aware of the existence of sharks in our seas only when screaming tabloid headlines give them a totally erroneous impression of these amazing and beautiful creatures. I realised that clearly there was a job to be done, and decided to make it my mission to bring the existence of our sharks to the widest possible audience. Also, I wanted to ensure that my audience realised that man is the threat to sharks and not the other way round.

My trying to find a book to give Craig had told me there wasn't one, so I realised there was a gap to fill and filling it would fit in with my mission. We've now started shark cage diving in Britain, generated a large number of sensible headlines, deployed the first satellite tags on Porbeagle sharks, and secured the first underwater Porbeagle images. Also, I've presented a Radio 4 shark series, and we've started to make films about British sharks - so the mission is well underway.

Researching and writing "Sharks in British Seas" taught me how little I knew about our sharks. I hope you enjoy reading the book as much as I've enjoyed putting it together.

Richard Peirce.

SHARKS
IN BRITISH SEAS

Foreword by Richard E Grant

Introduction by Richard Peirce

Thanks and acknowledgements

Illustrations – Photographs, maps, diagrams and cartoons

SECTION 1.

SECTION 2

Useful websites

Thanks and acknowledgements

About the author

Chapter One

THE WORLD OF SHARKS

Shark. There are few words that send a shiver down the spine so successfully. Peter Benchley's book Jaws, later made into a blockbuster film by Steven Spielberg, identified man's fears and played on them. The fear of being eaten alive, the fear of being outside your element and the fear of the unknown are all exploited menacingly in the early minutes of the film, when the first victim falls prey to attack. What can be more chilling than swimming on the surface of the ocean wondering what unseen dangers are lurking beneath you? This is the stuff of nightmares and truly terrifying.

Man has feared and demonised sharks since the earliest times. Many cultures with strong ties to the sea feature sharks prominently in their art and mythology. In the Cook and Solomon islands, sharks are worshipped; they appear in Australian aboriginal mythology; sharks play a central part in many Polynesian legends; and Hawaiians and Tahitians believe dead relatives can return in the form of sharks. In the Mediterranean, sharks also feature from early times in both Roman and ancient Greek literature. In the fifth century BC, Herodotus related how shipwrecked Persian sailors were eaten by sharks, and around 330 BC, Aristotle wrote in detail about sharks in his Historia Animalium, accurately describing the difference between them and bony fish.

By the start of the 20th century, sharks were firmly established as fearsome and loathsome predators. Shipwreck incidents in both world wars reconfirmed this outlook. When the USS Indianapolis was sunk in the Far East at the end of World War II, 900 men went into the water, but only 317 survived the sharks and the elements. Thereafter, the shark's position as a hate figure equalled that of any monster before or since.

There are at least 456 shark species in the world's oceans and around 30 can be found in British seas, but there are only a handful of recorded instances of attacks on man. Of the United Kingdom's shark species only the Mako, the Blue, the Thresher and the Porbeagle are recorded as being dangerous to man. However, with these species being depleted by more than 60 per cent due to overfishing, having the chance to see such magnificent animals must be regarded as a privilege, not something to provoke fear and media hysteria. Many will be surprised to learn that – in addition to Makos, Blues, Threshers, and Porbeagles – Hammerheads, Soupfin Sharks (Tope), Greenland Sharks, Sixgill and Sevengill Sharks are also on the 'British list'.

Fish are split into two main groups: Teleosts, which have bony skeletons and Chondrichthyes, which have skeletons made of cartilage. Sharks belong to the group Chondrichthyes or cartilaginous (non-bony) fishes. Chondrichthyan fishes are divided into two sub-groups: the Elasmobranchii and the Holocephali. Sharks are part of the former and there are eight Orders of sharks (see Section 2).

Sharks are superbly adapted to their environment. Light pliable cartilage instead of heavy dense bones, together with their highly streamlined shapes, promotes efficient movement. Our warm-blooded sharks such as the Mako, Thresher and Porbeagle often rely on speed to catch their prey. Others such as the Angel Sharks are ambush predators and depend on their camouflage to conceal them from their prey.

Sharks possess the same five senses as humans – smell, taste, touch, hearing and sight – although, in some instances, they work relatively better in their world than ours do in our environment. Experiments with Lemon and Nurse Sharks have established their olfactory ability to detect concentrations as low as one part per million. When working with Blue Sharks off North Cornwall, I lay 'chum' in the water. This is essentially a scent trail made of mashed up oily fish such as mackerel. (Incidentally, the English name for chum is rubby dubby). I very often have to wait several hours for Blue Sharks to find us. This not only illustrates their relative scarcity, but also indicates that, for our trail to be effective, we have to wait for it to cover several miles. When sharks have picked up the smell, they will swim up the trail looking for a meal. The concentration of chum materials in the water two or three miles from the boat is minute but the sharks still find us, thereby illustrating their acute sense of smell.

In addition to the five senses they share with us, sharks also have two extra senses: the lateral line, a mechanosensory system, and the ampullae of Lorenzini, an electrosensory system.

The lateral line extends from the head to the base of the tail (caudal) fin, and consists of a pair of tubes containing sets of sensory cells with protrusions known as neuromasts or hair cells. The hairs react to movement and changes in pressure. Working in conjunction with the lateral line are the pit organs, which are pockets scattered around the body that also contain sensory cells. These systems enable sharks to detect changes in pressure, tiny vibrations and water displacements, and to determine the direction from which they are coming.

The ampullae of Lorenzini make up an electrosensory system used to detect weak electrical fields. Elongated, jelly-filled tubes connect pores on the skin's surface to the ampullae, which contain receptor cells. These pores are clearly visible as dark dots below the snout and behind the eyes. I have many times seen Great White Sharks apparently attracted to, and investigating, metal items such as propellers and shark cages. This is quite possibly due to the objects' electrical fields. It is believed that Hammerheads may use a combination of their electrosensory and mechanosensory systems to detect prey buried in sand.

Sharks are carnivores with diets ranging from plankton to mammals, other sharks, large and small bony fish and invertebrates, including crustaceans. The dental array of sharks reflects this diet. The filter feeders (plankton eaters) have only tiny vestigial teeth, whereas the Great White has a formidable set of sharp triangular teeth perfectly suited to removing large chunks of flesh from their prey. The Mako has sharp, pointed, blade-like teeth ideal for tearing and trapping prey. Ocean bottom-dwelling sharks, which have crustaceans on their menu, have specialised teeth for crushing shells. A shark's mouth is a tooth factory, with new teeth being continuously formed in the gums inside the mouth and then moving outwards. The older teeth drop off making space for the new, which may last for anything from a month to a year.

Sharks breathe by extracting oxygen from the water as it passes over their gills. Water enters through the mouth, passes through the internal gill openings and is then expelled through the external gill outlet. There is less oxygen in water than in air, so sharks need to ensure a good, continual flow through their gills. Some species achieve this by using a system called 'ram ventilation', which forces water through the gills as the shark swims. Others rely on a combination of ram ventilation and a gill pump and often spend time motionless – either resting or sleeping on the sea floor – while the pump provides the flow of oxygenated water over their gills.

Assessing shark intelligence is extremely difficult but two things are known. Firstly, compared to many in the animal kingdom, sharks have large brains (and, as we have seen, they have two extra senses). Secondly, research carried out with Lemon and Nurse Sharks has shown that they can learn to perform actions, respond to stimuli and have memories.

In November 2003, a Great White Shark off the coast of South Africa in False Bay was fitted with a pop-off satellite tag that came away 6,897 miles away off Exmouth in Western Australia. The journey had taken 99 days and, for a large percentage of the time, the shark, a female, had been close to the surface. It is clear that she travelled a direct route and this suggests she possessed the ability to navigate, possibly using stellar clues. This was reinforced when she was recognised six months later back in False Bay. What had caused her to leave a well supplied feeding area and make her transoceanic journey? Her direct line travel there and back indicates she was on a mission, which she achieved before swimming home.

———————————

Mention shark behaviour to most people and it's more than likely that they will conjure up an image of aggression: attacks, feeding frenzies and threatening fins slicing through the water signalling a prelude to a strike. While it is true that most sharks spend much of their time hunting and eating, most feeding frenzies are man-induced, and attacks on humans are extremely rare. Typically, there are fewer than ten human deaths attributable to shark attacks in the whole world in a year. Recently, the number of reported shark-related deaths has been five or six a year. Bees, hippos, cars, alcohol, sex, over-exercise, under-exercise, snakes, earthquakes and almost anything else you can think of are more dangerous to man than sharks.

Sharks don't form family groups as such but some species do school. The Scalloped Hammerhead is well known for this behaviour and, in British waters, the Porbeagle does the same, making it very vulnerable to targeted fishing. The Spurdog (aka the Piked Dogfish or Spiny Dogfish) will also form aggregations. When schools or aggregations are created there will probably be social interactions but there has been very little research in this area. At certain times of the year Porbeagles aggregate by sex and this, in addition to the ease with which longline fishing boats can catch them, increases their vulnerability. Cooperative hunting has been observed in some species such as the Sevengill Shark and there is anecdotal evidence of this activity involving Great Whites, Porbeagles, Threshers, Oceanic Whitetips, Sand Tigers and some Reef Sharks.

The popular perception is that mammals are warm-blooded and fish cold-blooded. However, some sharks including the Great White, Porbeagle, Mako and Thresher maintain a body temperature of a constant level above that of the surrounding water. This is achieved through a heat exchange system known as the 'rete mirabile' or 'marvellous net', which is a network of tiny capillaries. Cold oxygenated blood from the gills runs parallel but in the opposite direction to deoxygenated blood warmed by muscle action returning to the gills. These vessels running alongside each other exchange heat highly effectively, with no heat loss to the sea.

Most sharks possess a tough and durable skin that man has turned into various leather articles and has also been used as sandpaper. Embedded in a shark's skin are small, sharp, teeth-like scales known as dermal denticles, which fall out but are replaced continuously during life. As well as providing physical protection, dermal denticles create a surface that has virtually no surface drag. Top swimmers wearing Speedo bodysuits to eliminate drag are emulating this shark characteristic. The largest shark, which is also the largest fish in the sea, is the Whale Shark, known to reach lengths of up to 15 metres (46 feet). At the other end of the scale, the tiny Pigmy Shark measures just 15 centimetres (six inches). Neither of these is found in our waters – our sharks range from the giant Basking Shark, the second largest fish in the world achieving lengths of over 10 metres (30 feet), down to the Velvet Belly measuring 60 centimetres (two feet). Along the way, there is the 5.5 metre plus (18 feet) Greenland Shark, the Sharpnose Sevengill, the Bluntnose Sixgill, the Kitefin Shark (aka Dark Charlie), the Bramble Shark, the Angel Shark and many others, including the more widely recognised Hammerheads, Makos, Threshers, Porbeagles and Blues.

Britain's shores are washed by the North Sea, Irish Sea, Celtic Sea, English Channel, the Bristol Channel, the sea of the Hebrides, and the Atlantic Ocean. Together, they provide a huge diversity of marine environments that can support abundant populations of sharks. Sadly though, despite these riches, the extinction clock is ticking for many of our species due to over-exploitation by man. Britain has led the world In many initiatives, and I hope that we can play a leading role in protecting not just the sharks in our waters but those around the world.

The earliest sharks appeared on the planet some 400 million years ago. There is something unbalanced – indeed almost criminal – in the thought that the recently-arrived species called mankind should be responsible for threatening the extinction of sharks. The main reason the extinction clock is ticking so close to midnight is the overfishing of sharks to satisfy the demand from the Far East for fins for soup. The rapid economic development of the Chinese and other Far Eastern economies has brought luxuries within reach of an ever-increasing consumer market. Sharks really are in the soup, bowls of this expensive dull-tasting delicacy being largely responsible for pushing one of earth's oldest inhabitants to the verge of extinction.

Chapter Two

THE GREAT WHITE ENIGMA

Why isn't the Great White Shark a permanent resident in British waters? Conditions are broadly similar to those where large resident populations flourish, such as South Africa, southern Australia, and California. The nearest confirmed Great White Shark to our waters was the capture in 1977 of a female in the Northern Bay of Biscay off La Rochelle – 168 nautical miles from Land's End. In 2003/04, a female Great White nicknamed Nicole completed a six-month, 13,000+ mile journey from False Bay in South Africa to Western Australia, where she turned around and then swam back to South Africa. So, clearly, 168 miles is no distance for these sharks.

Fishermen's stories are renowned for their colour and exaggeration. By the mid 1990's, I realised that I was continually hearing stories of large, powerful, unidentified sharks in UK waters. Could some of them be Great Whites? There was no reason why not, so I started logging each report.

My record keeping has not included all the reports I have received, because some claimed sightings were so ludicrous they weren't worth noting or considering further. However, from 1996 until the time of writing I can certainly say that I have heard of between 70 and 80 possible Great White Shark encounters. Of those, seven that I have investigated remain credible after further examination. I am not saying that these seven incidents involved Great Whites, but the descriptions given certainly fit those of Great White Sharks.

So do these sharks visit our shores or not? The jury is out and will remain so until firm proof exists – a carcass, tooth, tissue sample, photograph or some other conclusive evidence. However, there is a high probability that the creatures involved in some of the following incidents were indeed Great White Sharks.

LOOE, CORNWALL: JULY 1970

John Reynolds, a Looe-based shark angling skipper, had been at sea all day about eight miles offshore with baited lines out and two rubby dubby bags dangling in the water. In that year Porbeagle and Blue Shark numbers were much higher than they are now, so it was unusual that they had not seen one all day. John's theory is that the lack of other sharks might have indicated the presence of of a larger predator.

At sometime around 3pm John started to take in his lines and rubby dubby bags in preparation for returning to shore. He was pulling in the stern bag when a large shark appeared only a few feet behind the boat.

The animal looked straight at John, staying in a head-up position for some seconds before slipping back into the water and disappearing. John saw only the head but his description fits a Great White Shark and it is the only shark commonly known to spy-hop, which is the action of putting its head out of the water. Spy-hopping has rarely been observed in non-baited conditions and may not be natural behaviour. Current opinion suggests it is a response to concentrated scent stimuli at the surface like chum lines, and not an attempt to espy objects above the surface as has been previously thought. Spy-hopping is also practised by some whales but I have never heard of any of our existing shark species doing this.

The incident described by John fits a Great White Shark spy-hopping.

PADSTOW, NORTH CORNWALL: AUGUST 1999

A leaked tip-off to the national press about the sighting of a large shark thought to be a Great White up the coast from Padstow near Crackington Haven resulted in a hysterical reaction and, at times, insulting scepticism. This combination made the fishing party involved dismayed that the story ever got out.

Mike Turner and Phil Britts, who were aboard the Blue Fox together with Phil's wife, Rhona, and others all saw a large shark about 37 metres (40 yards) away. The dorsal fin was clearly visible approaching them in a straight line as they were releasing an earlier-caught Soupfin Shark (Tope).

The shark, estimated to be 4.6 metres (15 feet) long, passed the stern and rolled, revealing a clear white underside separated from the grey/brown topside by a jagged line. It was visible for about a minute, having, at its nearest, come within 2 metres of the boat. Those on board believed that it had probably taken the Soupfin Shark (Tope) before disappearing.

A large black eye was noted and this, together with the colours and morphology described, are consistent with a Great White Shark. Mike had seen many Great

Whites in South Africa and is adamant about the precision of his sighting. The others on board had seen a number of Porbeagles and Basking Sharks and ruled those out. It is noted that the proactive behaviour displayed in approaching the boat also fits the actions of a Great White Shark.

CAMBEAK HEAD, NORTH CORNWALL: AUGUST 1999

The Blue Fox incident took place off Cambeak Head, and the following day there was a similar occurrence in exactly the same location. Paul Vincent was out with his friend Jason Coe fishing for Soupfin Shark (Tope) from his 5.2 metre (17 foot) dory, Blissful. Paul had hooked a Soupfin Shark (Tope), and was about to lift it aboard using his gaff hook when a very large shark appeared and bit off the bottom two thirds of the Soupfin Shark (Tope) before swimming off. Paul estimates that it was at least as long as his boat. His full description was a match for the shark seen by those aboard the Blue Fox: the same grey/brown dorsal side, white ventral side, large triangular dorsal fin, black eye and unhurried, investigative behaviour.

TINTAGEL HEAD, NORTH CORNWALL: SEPTEMBER 1999

Less than two weeks after these incidents and about 12 miles away near Tintagel Head, a lobster fisherman found a very large shark tangled up in his rope. He asked to remain anonymous — although his identity is known to me — and the whole incident I am about to describe was witnessed. When hauling in his pots there was what he thought was a snag in the line. It freed itself and then something hit the back of the davit. He went to look and saw the tail fin of a shark about 4.6 metres (15 feet) long. Because of its size, he thought it must be a Basking Shark.

Sharks cannot swim backwards and, if they land up in a rope, they often twist and become thoroughly entangled. Death follows unless they are freed quickly. And, unfortunately, that was the fate of this creature. As it had no commercial value, the only thing to do was to cut it loose. It was seen to have a slate grey topside and, as it was freed, it rolled showing a pure white underside. It also had what was described as a crescent-shaped mouth and triangular teeth. Basking Sharks and Porbeagles were both familiar to those on board and they were sure it was neither of those. At 4.6 metres (15 feet) what else could it have been? A Blue Shark or a Porbeagle? Very unlikely. A Mako? Again unlikely, and the colours and teeth as described don't fit.

So, three sharks each estimated to be the same size, each broadly fitting the same description and their sightings separated by only three weeks and 12 miles. Coincidence? Same shark? A Great White Shark?

August 2007. Hoax photo on the front page of the Newquay Guardian.

The incidents that remain credible following investigation are clustered in two areas of the British Isles

A Great White Shark up close. © Richard Peirce

QUIES ISLANDS, NORTH CORNWALL: JULY 2002

On a clear, almost windless day Brian Bate was laying his lobster pots to the northeast of the Quies Islands, when, suddenly, a large fish between 3.6 metres (12 feet) and 4.6 metres (15 feet) in length leapt completely out of the water with something in its mouth. Brian went to the spot and found a large spreading pool of blood with pieces of seal blubber floating in it. Seagulls were already feeding on the smaller pieces of blubber.

Leaping out of the water is called breaching and what Brian saw was a typical breaching attack, the size, body shape and colours precisely fitting a Great White Shark. When I showed him various photographs of breaching sharks, including those of Makos and Threshers, he identified the Great White.

I suggested to him that it was a pity he hadn't retrieved one of the larger pieces of blubber in case a tooth might have been lodged in it or the bite mark could have been identified. He told me that he didn't have a boathook and no sane person who had seen what he had would have started putting their hands in the water fishing around for bits of blubber!

If it wasn't a Great White, what else could it have been? For various reasons based on Brian's description, Blues, Porbeagles and Makos can be ruled out, which leaves a Killer Whale (Orca) as the only other possibility. Brian had seen many Orcas and was quite sure that wasn't the case.

The triangular teeth of a Great White Shark and the sawing action of the jaws make dismemberment a typical occurrence, while this does not happen with the other sharks mentioned.

Two days after Brian Bate saw his 'breaching shark' kill a seal, a lone yachtsman sailed up the coast from Newquay to Padstow. He later recounted how a large shark followed in his wake for the greater part of his journey and how he had sailed through the same water where Brian had seen the breaching attack. He is familiar with Basking Shark fins and is certain the shark that followed him was not one of those.

I went chumming in the Quies area with Brian two weeks after the seal predation and there were no seals to be seen where, normally, there is a small colony of between 15 and 20. The general area around Trevose Head, the Quies, the Camel Estuary and the offshore islands is home to several small population pockets of seals, but they did not return to the area until early October. I was alerted to two cases of washed-up seal remains, one in July before the Bates incident and the other in early August. Both carcasses consisted of only partial remains and both were extensively bird-pecked, making it impossible to determine how the seals died or learn anything from the wounds.

WESTERN ISLES, SCOTLAND: JULY 2003

To most people the idea of finding a Great White in Scottish waters would be no less improbable than finding the Loch Ness monster. Dr Simon Greenstreet was diving near Ullapool at the western edge of the Summer Isles, near Black Rock, on 4 July 2003. With him were his wife Wendy and two other divers in a 5.2 metre (17 foot) rigid inflatable boat. The Greenstreets had just finished their dive and the next pair were kitting up when a large fin was spotted some 28-36 metres (30–40 yards) away. The obvious thought was that it was a Basking Shark.

With the opportunity of swimming with a harmless shark in mind, Dr Greenstreet moved the boat closer. As soon as the engine started, the shark changed course and moved purposefully towards the boat. At this point, those on board still assumed it was a Basking Shark but, although nothing was said, doubts were creeping in.

When it was only 14 metres (15 yards) from the boat, the bulk of the shark was apparent. The distance from dorsal to tail fin was estimated at nearly three metres (9 feet). At that stage, the boat party realised this was no Basking Shark but it continued its approach, eventually swimming alongside only about half a metre away.

Those aboard judged the shark to be more than 4.6 metres (15 feet) in length. Dr Greenstreet has no specific shark interests but has seen enough Basking Sharks to know their particular characteristics. Unlike a Basking Shark, this one had a clearly defined white ventral side, a large solid broad-based triangular dorsal fin, a light grey dorsal side with clearly defined worn patches and smaller gills than the very large distinctive ones on a Basking Shark.

The description fits that of a Great White, as does its proactive behaviour in coming towards the boat when the engine was started. I believe that Dr Greenstreet and his party saw a Great White Shark.

NORTH EAST SCOTLAND: DECEMBER 2003

Five months after Dr Greenstreet's experience near Ullapool, a fisherman working off North East Scotland caught a large shark in his net. He did not wish to be named but I have interviewed him and others corroborate his story. What they all described was a large shark, 5.5 - 5.8 metres (18 - 19 feet) long with a large triangular dorsal fin snapping at small fish while it was trapped in the net. Teeth were observed but there is no accurate description of them and the gills were not seen in sharp enough detail to be definitive. The fisherman was trying to work out how to free the shark when it managed to free itself.

The fisherman is not saying this was a Great White Shark, but he is adamant that it was not a Basking Shark. This does not leave many options and, as I had a photograph, I decided to send it to colleagues and seek their opinions. The image went to Great White shark experts Ian Fergusson, Craig Ferreira, Jeremy Stafford-Deitsch, Leonard Compagno, Rolf Cyabaiski and others. Ian Fergusson and Leonard Compagno, two of the world's leading experts, collaborated in their reply and shared the opinion that, had I not told them the location was Scotland, but instead had said South Africa, southern Australia, or California, their first choice of identity would have been a Great White. However, because I had said "Scotland", they started thinking what else it might have been.

This is interesting. If I had simply said "I think this is a Great White; what do you think?", there is a good chance that two globally-renowned shark experts would have stuck to their original identification and the photograph would now be the first likely proof of a Great White in British waters.

NORTH UIST, SCOTLAND: JULY 2005

Modern languages school teacher Philip Harding, his colleague Alan and Alan's two teenage children were trolling for Pollock two miles south of Locheport at Aignish Point on the east coast of North Uist when Philip cut the engine to set up rods. At this point, a very large shark came up vertically beside the boat and had a good look at those on board before slowly diving and disappearing.

The features noticed were:
- a dark grey/bronzy dorsal side

- a pure white ventral side, so white that, for a split second, Philip thought the creature was an Orca before realising that it was a shark

- the shark was the length of the boat – 4.9 metres (16 feet)

- a very large girth and a solid (non-floppy), pointed, triangular dorsal fin

Philip and Alan are both very familiar with Basking Sharks and are quite adamant this was not one of those. However, the next day, just to be sure, Philip went to look at a freshly-dead Basking Shark caught in a net off Lochmaddy. Thereafter, he was able to confirm his initial impression that the morphology of the two sharks was markedly different in many respects.

Philip is certain that the animal he encountered was a Great White and, while he did not share this opinion with his boating colleagues on the day because he did not wish to alarm the youngsters, they have subsequently discussed the encounter and are all in agreement with his opinion.

Common and Grey Seals are abundant in that area and, to the west of North Uist, Monach Island has what is thought to be the largest seal colony in Europe.

WESTERN ISLES SCOTLAND: JUNE 2007

Mathematician and marine scientist Jim Watson told me in June 2007 that he had been hearing regular reports of Great White Sharks in the Minch and Little Minch over the previous ten years. This fits with three of the more compelling accounts mentioned in this chapter. The Minch would be an ideal place for Great White Sharks: several Grey Seal colonies, and shoals of Haddock, Mackerel, Cod, Herring and Pollock provide an adequate food source, and the water temperatures (with summer highs of 16°C and winter lows of 5°-6°C) are comfortably within the tolerance range for these sharks for much of the year.

Jim has made more than 3000 dives and has worked extensively in the waters around the Hebrides off and on throughout his life. He accepts the possible presence of Great White Sharks in the Minch in an almost matter-of-fact manner. I formed the impression that he would be more surprised by the suggestion that they were not there than they were there.

Jim suggested I contact the Hebridean Whale and Dolphin Trust to see if it had any anecdotal or actual evidence of the presence of Great Whites. I spoke at length to Dr Peter Stevick and became interested when he offered to send me a picture of a large shark caught in the Minch some years ago and hitherto unidentified. The photograph turned out to be of a Mako, so there was no new evidence to add to my files.

SOUND OF HARRIS, SCOTLAND: LATE JUNE/EARLY JULY 2007

Film footage taken in the Sound of Harris on a mobile phone, possibly showing a shark attacking a seal, was sent to the Marine Conservation Society for comment in September 2007. Thereafter, it was passed on to the Shark Trust.

I have examined the footage as have the following other experts: Ian Fergusson, Jeremy Stafford-Deitsch, Leonard Compagno, Henry Mollet and Chris Fallows. I have also interviewed one of the eyewitnesses to the event.

Fergusson and Compagno both felt that the percentage likelihood in favour of the shark being a Great White Shark was 60 per cent while there was a 40 per cent possibility of it being a Shortfin Mako. The other three felt it could be either but favoured a Shortfin Mako. My own view is that it was either a Shortfin Mako or, possibly, a Porbeagle.

The witness, Darren Steadwood, was at sea with two friends when extensive splashing in the water 18 metres away attracted their attention. They went to investigate and discovered a seal thrashing about on the surface. They were in a deep channel and could see it apparently being tossed about but didn't catch sight of a shark other than occasional glimpses of what might have been a fin. The video seems to show blood but Darren doesn't remember seeing any at the time.

Darren's friend recorded the incident on his mobile phone. The activity stopped and nothing happened for about 30 seconds and then a fin broke the surface between seven and nine metres away. They went to investigate as the shark swam away from them. Then it turned and swam towards the boat, going underneath it and then disappearing. There was no sign of the seal, or any seal remains, which may indicate that it had survived the attack and escaped if, indeed, it was an attack.

Darren estimated the length of the shark at three metres or just over, and recalls a stout body with a dark grey black dorsal (top) side. No gills were noticed. Darren did not get a view of the shark's underside and does not remember seeing its eyes. His initial impression was not of the seal being attacked but of animals playing or maybe feeding.

The footage shows a dorsal fin appearing from the left of the screen. The fin appears to have a slightly rounded apex with a straight down trailing edge and a curved forward edge. At this stage, the dorsal shape is certainly more representative of a Great White Shark than that of a Shortfin Mako. However, as the shark continues to move the footage becomes confusing because, at some angles, the apex of the dorsal appears more rounded. A caudal fin then comes into view and the shark at this point is swimming directly away from the photographer still moving across the screen from left to right.

There is still nothing conclusive and the next good 'side on' dorsal view shows a fin with a more rounded than pointed apex. The shark keeps swimming towards the right, disappears, then a caudal fin reappears followed by the dorsal. Thereafter, it turns around and starts swimming from the right to the left on an interception track with the boat.

The next good 'side on' of the dorsal once again seems to say "Great White Shark", with a more pointed apex and a straight-down, perhaps even slightly concave, trailing edge. The shark is swimming quite fast and possibly displaying excited behaviour. The seal has by now disappeared, so there is a possibility that the presence of seals out of sight below the water is influencing the shark's behaviour. The shark then swims right up to the vessel, possibly making contact with the hull, before swimming underneath, which is where the footage ends.

The shark could have been a Great White Shark but, equally, it could have been a Shortfin Mako or, possibly, a Porbeagle. It is interesting to note, however, that potential Great White Shark incidents that retain credibility after investigation are clustered in two areas: North Cornwall and the Western Isles (the Minch, Little Minch).

There are only two possible White Shark incidents outside these areas that I am aware of — the Pentland Firth 'net capture and escape in 2004', and the possible spy-hopping off Looe in the 1970s.

ST IVES, CORNWALL: JULY 2007

On Thursday 26 July, Dr Oliver Crimmen was shown a clip of amateur video by the Sun newspaper. It was taken on a video camcorder by Nick Fletcher while holidaying in St Ives. The film showed a small pod of Common Dolphins making their way along the coast and, at the end of the sequence, a creature is clearly seen to breach. Dr Crimmen was quoted as saying: "It's definitely predatory and definitely big. I can't rule out a Great White."

I, too, was asked to confirm the identity. But it was impossible because the film was not clear enough. All that could be seen for sure was that it was a fish somewhere between 2.4 metres (8 feet) and 3.6 metres (12 feet) long doing a half-to-three-quarters breach displaying a white ventral side. Given the close presence of dolphins, they must come into the reckoning as must Basking, Porbeagle and Mako sharks.

If, as I do, you believe that Great Whites are occasional visitors to our shores then that possibility cannot be ruled out. However, saying they can't be ruled out is a long way from confirming that the image showed a Great White Shark, which is what the Sun inferred that I had done.

This sparked an extraordinary media frenzy and the Sun managed to string it out for a further eight days with all the other nationals and many regional papers joining in. Both the Monday and Tuesday editions of the Sun carried front page pictures of Basking Shark's dorsal fins slicing through the waters off St Ives with various 'experts' identifying the fins as belonging to Great Whites. By Thursday, the Newquay Guardian's front page carried a picture of a Great White said to be taken off Towan Head, Newquay (See page 12). This was the first picture of a Great White to appear, but interest was waning and various other reports were hinting at doubts over where the photograph was taken. The photograph was later admitted to be a hoax.

During this time, the people of St Ives were, understandably, cashing in. Shark spotting boat trips were packed with excited tourists. Virtually everything that could float was taking to the sea to look for sharks. Cafes had maps of St Ives Bay on their walls with all the sightings marked. Shark ice creams, T-shirts and even shark-shaped pasties were produced to add to the fun and make the tills ring more frequently.

Nick Fletcher's original film clip had been forgotten by the time the story died. This was probably the most intense and long-running shark saga ever in the UK press, but was by no means based on compelling evidence.

The question remains: do Great White Sharks ever visit British waters? For me, the answer is "probably yes". However, there is still no hard evidence and, owing to the massive depletion rates the species has suffered (about 80 per cent), the chances of any such visit are slim and getting slimmer.

Chapter Three

SHARK ANGLING

Very few holidaymakers who visited Cornwall in 1961 are likely to have been aware that 6,286 sharks were caught by anglers off the county's coast that year. It was the highest annual number ever recorded by the Shark Angling Club based in Looe. Most of the catch were Blue Sharks, but in those days Mako, Porbeagle and Thresher Sharks were also caught regularly on rod and line.

Before 1953, comparatively few sharks were caught by recreational anglers in British waters. However, in 1952 the use of "rubby dubby" started to become widespread, and the Shark Angling Club of Great Britain was founded the following year. "Rubby dubby" is the British name used to describe what most of the rest of the world calls "chum" or, in Australia, "burley". Chumming, rubby dubbying and burleying all describe the laying of a scent trail in the water by using mashed-up oily fish such as mackerel and pilchard. They are placed in net bags and hung over the side of the boat. After a time, the oil floats to the surface, and the small pieces of fish that work their way through the mesh sink in the water. The heavier pieces sink faster and further while the lighter ones stay closer to the surface. The overall effect is that of a multi-layered scent highway. Many anglers add bran to the mixture. That also sinks in the water and it is believed to help the effectiveness of the chum trail.

The founding of the Shark Angling Club quickly established Looe as the "shark capital" of Britain, and, in the 1950s and 1960s, its shark angling fleet consisted of 25 full-time boats during the June to October season. Mevagissey, Polperro, Porthleven, Newlyn and Penzance also had shark angling fleets, and boats started working from Padstow, Boscastle and Bude on the north Cornish coast, as well as out of north and south Devon and some ports in Dorset.

In the mid-1960s, a dozen boats worked out of the Isle of Wight and Portsmouth targeting Threshers and Porbeagles. Today, Isle of Wight shark anglers rarely see a Porbeagle; Threshers have become their most commonly encountered species.The Pembrokeshire coast has long been a good place to catch Blue Sharks, and, in recent years, numbers caught there have, on a pro rata number of boats basis, been higher than anywhere else in the UK. Porbeagles are also caught there and the occasional Mako is encountered. Many North East coastal ports including, Whitby, Hartlepool and Bridlington, have attracted shark anglers, with Soupfin Shark (Tope) being the main target, although Porbeagles have become more recent additions.

The world record for a Porbeagle Shark catch – 230 kgs (507 lbs) - was established by Chris Bennett in the Pentland Firth in March 1993. Shark angling was started in The Highlands in 1992 by the now defunct Big Game Club of Scotland with the Pentland Firth port of Scrabster serving as the base of activities. Chris is still shark angling and reports a good population of Porbeagles in the area, where live bait, Cod or Pollock is used instead of rubby dubby.

The shark most highly prized by anglers is probably the Mako. The British record Mako - weighing 227 kgs (500 lbs) - was caught off Looe in 1971 by Mrs J Yallop (see plate 26).

It has already been mentioned that Porbeagles, Makos and Threshers are caught in much lower numbers than Blue Sharks. However, what these four species have in common in angling terms is that they are all caught by using rubby dubby, whereas Smoothhounds, Stary Smoothhounds, Nursehounds (aka Bull Huss) and Piked Dogfish (Spurdogs) are caught near the seabed without rubby dubby. Tope are also commonly caught off the bottom, too, but do respond to rubby dubby. Also known as the Soupfin Shark and the School Shark, the Tope is found off all Britain's coasts.

Since 1961, Looe Shark Angling Club figures for shark catches have crashed and, in 2007, only 142 Blue Sharks were caught. The regular incidence of Mako, Porbeagle and Threshers has now become sporadic. There is no Shark Angling Club record of a Mako being caught since the 1970's and a juvenile Porbeagle caught in 2002 was the first caught by a club boat for many years. Juvenile Threshers caught in 2005 and 2007 were also the first for several years. In fact, all of the species targeted by anglers in British waters have suffered severe population declines owing to commercial fishing pressures.

Trevor Housby's book "Shark Fishing in British Waters" (published in 1972) describes the Isle of Wight as the 'top Porbeagle hotspot yet discovered'. Danny Vokins is, perhaps, the most successful current Isle of Wight shark angler and he hasn't seen a Porbeagle in island waters since 1996. Blue and Soupfin (Tope) Sharks were so common in the 1960s that they were almost unchallenging nuisances to many anglers; today, they are highly prized. Housby's Isle of Wight top Porbeagle hotspot has become the best place in the British seas to catch Threshers and in

The Shark Angling Club can be found on the quay in east Looe. © Shark Angling Club

Mrs Yallop with her British record Mako in 1971. © Shark Angling Club

J Pottier with his 211kg (465lbs) Porbeagle caught in 1976. © Shark Angling Club

Unti 1994 all sharks were brought back to Looe for weighing. Weight is now estimated at sea and sharks released. © Shark Angling Club

A Blue Shark loses its battle. All SAC GB sharks are now released. © Shark Angling Club

Most Britons are unaware of the existence of large sharks in British waters. © *Shark Angling Club*

2006 twelve were caught and tagged, while the figure for 2007 was twenty. I have talked about Porbeagles at greater length in Chapter 7 so suffice it is to say here that most Porbeagle angling hotspots quickly become cold spots once the word gets out and longliners move in.

ANGLING EQUIPMENT

Much has been written about the equipment used by anglers to catch sharks. Brigadier J.A.L. Caunter, founder of the Shark Angling Club, stated that rods should be about seven foot long with plenty of play in the tip and strength in the butt. J.H. Bennet, in Big Game Angling, describes a rod as a spring between the fish, the power of the angler and the breaking strain of the line.

A visit to a London tackle shop acquainted me with a bewildering and diverse selection of big game rods. However, there are two basic types: the "stand up stick", a short, powerful rod used mainly for big game fish which dive deep and the more common six-to-seven foot flexible rod that comes either in one or two pieces. The longer, more flexible rods are favoured by British shark anglers as they are better at coping with sharks making long runs near the surface and/or going under the boat from side to side. Early rods were made of hardwood, generally hickory. Thereafter, the progression went from copper, tubular steel, hollow glass and solid glass before manufacturers created today's carbon-fibre structures.

I am bound to upset someone if I say that American big game reels lead the world but it does seem that way. Wherever in the world I have talked to shark and big game anglers, I have come across the name Penn, short for the Penn Fishing Tackle and Manufacturing Company of Pennsylvania, or that of Shakespeare, which now appears to be the dominant force in reel manufacturing. Today's reels are complex, hi-tech pieces of kit fitted with brakes, drag governors, harness lugs and clutches. They are made of non-rust materials and often offer two speeds. Prices for heavy duty Penn reels range from £300 to £1500, so dropping a borrowed shark rod over the side should be avoided if one values one's friendship!

Big game angling, including shark angling, is all about using the lightest line to catch the biggest fish. This ensures a battle of skill rather than a contest of strength. Basically, if the angler is not good enough and relies only on brute force the line will break and the fish will be lost. Sharks can easily bite through monofilament lines so, to prevent this, steel traces are used between the hook and the line. Yesterday's large, brutal barbed J-shaped hooks have been replaced by circle and barbless hooks, which are biodegradable. These are designed to avoid deep or gut hooking sharks thus making removal easier.

CHANGING TIMES

In the 1960s in Looe it must have seemed as if the seas produced an endless supply of sharks. Most evenings during the season visitors to the quayside would have seen sharks hung up outside the Shark Angling Club (SAC) to be weighed and photographed with their captors. The following day most of the sharks were taken out to sea and dumped. In the 1960s and 1970s annual SAC catches of between 2,000 and 4,000 were usual. Throughout that period the club fleet comprised of 18–20 boats, all of which spent most of the season engaged in sharking.

Change was on the way though, and it arrived in 1976, when a catch of 928 was recorded compared with 2083 the previous year. This dramatic reduction of more than 50 per cent from one year to the next heralded a decline in numbers that bottomed out at 86 caught in the year 2000. However, shark angling is not responsible for the decline as numbers caught by anglers around the world are insignificant compared with the tens of millions taken by industrial fishing. Having said that, even before the "crash of 76" attitudes in Looe were changing with more and more sharks being released each year.

Between 1972 and 1976, the first tag-and-release programme was conducted as a joint effort by Dr John Stevens and the Shark Angling Club (the venture was part of Dr Stevens' Phd project) and 2,883 sharks – Blues, Soupfin Sharks (Tope), Porbeagles, and a Shortfin Mako - were tagged. Some years later the Jack Daniel's whiskey company took up sponsoring the next tag-and-release programme and all those returning tags with the requested information were rewarded with a bottle of whiskey. That sponsorship ended in 1995 and, from then on, all sharks caught were released unrecorded until tagging resumed under my sponsorship in August 1999.

To qualify to join the Shark Angling Club, an angler must land a catch weighing a minimum of 75lbs. This used to mean that all sharks that appeared to attain that weight or more had to be killed and weighed to enable new members to qualify. But, as I mentioned, attitudes were changing, and, in 1994, the club passed new rules involving a formula that enabled skippers to estimate weight based on length and girth. This rule came in specifically to stop the need for killing - unless a record was suspected, in which case the fish still had to be weighed. Other than "suspected" records, the club now operates a 100 per cent release policy and most skippers take part in the tagging programme.

One seeming contradiction among hunters of animals on land and sea is the respect and affection in which they regard their quarry. So the question is: why catch it if you love it? I suspect that question would get 10 different answers from 10 different individuals but what would be uniform is the respect that I have observed first hand among 99 per cent of the shark anglers I know. One man who long lined large numbers of Porbeagles in December 2003 attracted widespread condemnation, with shark anglers being among the loudest critics. In August 2007, another longliner caught more than 60 sharks near Lundy Island and he, too, was universally derided by anglers. Those who take up shark angling as a blood sport are quickly singled out by skippers and there is a virtual black list of people they will not take out again. Thankfully, it's a short list.

Changing attitudes have brought about differences to equipment, with the use of circle and barbless hooks now being the norm. Also, not all Looe skippers will tag sharks as some feel that removing the animals from the "support' of the water causes damage to organs that can prove fatal. This is correct and most skippers bring only the smaller sharks onboard, while tagging the larger ones over the side of the boat. All skippers are highly competent and hook removal, tagging, and measuring is done in the minimum of time. Survival rates among released Blue Sharks is thought by the Shark Angling Club to be near 100 per cent although it might possibly be less in the case of Porbeagles.

When a tagged shark is re-caught, the fisherman will find the tag has a "message in a bottle system", which offers a $15 reward for letting the club know the length of the shark and the latitude and longitude of its re-catch position. As it happens, 99.9 per cent of returns are from Spanish longliners operating in the Bay of Biscay and between the Azores and the Canaries. However, in 2002, the club was told about a female Blue Shark re-caught off the New Hampshire coast while other returns have come from the USA, South America and South Africa. Therefore, it can be clearly seen that tag and release helps establish migration patterns and provides information about growth rates.

Like others all over the world engaged in eco-tourism and leisure, the Shark Angling Club recognises the economic importance of sharks. The Great White Shark has become a recognised and valued asset in the South African Western Cape and the Blue Shark has been part of Looe's economy for 50 years. So the more it's recognised that sharks have a greater value alive rather than dead, the more recruits will swell conservationist ranks.

To recap:
- Six thousand sharks caught each year off Looe has become fewer than 200

- Eighteen full-time boats have decreased to 12 or 14 part-timers

- An almost total kill has become no kill

- The thriving drift net pilchard industry that attracted sharks and triggered them becoming targets for anglers has disappeared

- Hook sizes and designs have altered and angling club rules have changed

- Trophy photos have given way to tags

Hopefully, commercial fishing policies will now change too, and shark numbers will start to recover. If they do, no organisation will be happier than the Shark Angling Club.

Chapter Four

HUNTING THE GIANTS
Basking Shark Fisheries

Since the dawn of time man has hunted large animals. Mammoths, elephants, buffalo, and whales have all fallen prey to his traps, spears, arrows, snares and harpoons. However, early man did not kill for sport but to survive, finding uses for every part of his prey's body.

Reaching sizes of more than nine metres and weights of six to seven tonnes, the Basking Shark is truly a giant. The second largest fish in the world is a harmless plankton feeder, which at times has been hunted extensively. Man has found many uses for this gentle giant, including liver oil used as a lubricant and lamp oil, whilst squalene extracted from the oil has been used in cosmetics. Its skin has served as sandpaper and been used in making leather goods, while insulin has been extracted from the pancreas, flesh has been converted into fish meal and fins have ended up in soup. But perhaps the most bizarre use man has yet found for Basking Sharks was during in the Second World War, when Hurricane fighter pilots training in Scotland sometimes used them for target practise.

The first recorded Basking shark fishery was on the island of Canna in the Sea of the Hebrides. Fisheries came and went probably due to fluctuations in abundance and market conditions for the products, and the peak of Basking Shark fishing in British seas was in the 1950s. Anthony Watkins was operating a fishery before the Second World War based at Carradale in the Kintyre Peninsula on the Firth of Clyde. He concentrated mainly on the oil extracted and was the first man to realise that static factories would not work. That was a mistake made by Gavin Maxwell – best known as author of the acclaimed wildlife book "Ring of Bright Water" - when he set up his factory on the island of Soay and it was probably one of the major factors in the failure of that enterprise. Watkins went to fight in the war and resumed his activities afterwards. He was the first man to operate a factory ship, which accompanied his fleet of three or four catcher boats, and a few remnants of his business about half-a-mile north of the little harbour at Port Crannaich exist to this day.

The rendering plant had to be sited far enough away from human habitation for the stench not to affect local people. Watkins concentrated on the livers and the remainder of the carcass was dumped and left to rot. His three boats ranged widely from the Firth of Clyde to the Hebrides during July, August and early September. In later years, in addition to the rendering plant, the Watkins factory ship was kitted out to be able to handle the livers as well, and, as a result, he could barrel his oil at sea and dispatch it to the mainland point of sale.

Basking Sharks were always harpooned and guns were mounted in the bows of the catching boats as was the case with whaling ships. Barbed harpoons were originally the most widely used and the Norwegian Kongsberg was considered the most successful gun. The harpoon was aimed either just behind or just ahead of the dorsal fin, the idea being to penetrate the body cavity. When the harpoon was pulled back the semi tubular barbs opened giving the harpoon a fix. As soon as the shark was harpooned it would dive for the bottom. Up to one hundred fathoms of stout five/seven centimetres thick manila rope would be fixed to the harpoon with the other end secured to the catching boat. Big sharks would often take their captors for a ride before dying. In later years, barrels were attached to the rope end, which effectively marked the harpooned sharks, leaving catching boats free to pursue further kills, returning later to collect their earlier victims.

It is possible that up to 100,000 Basking Sharks were killed in the Northeast Atlantic, including the British Isles, over the past century, but during both world wars there were let ups, which to a small degree allowed numbers to recover. However, after World War Two a lot of things in Britain were in short supply, and Basking Shark oil fetched very good prices. One third of the volume of a Basking Shark is its bilobal (two lobes) liver, which contains the oil. The liver acts as a hepatic float that helps control flotation and buoyancy. Oil extraction was achieved either by rendering (boiling down) or by using centrifuges.

In addition to the fisheries in the Hebrides and off the West coast of Ireland, some attempts were made to catch these giants off Cornwall. Colin Speedie, the Basking Shark researcher and conservationist, tells of an incident involving a boat in the 1930s. A small powerboat went out from Portscatho and harpooned a shark that then towed the crew 16 miles out to sea before they had to cut it free to avoid ending up in Ireland or the United States! In the 1960s a Cornish pig farmer killed about 16 sharks and landed them on the flats at Mylor with a view to cutting them up and using them for pig feed. But one got some revenge, having been kicked by the farmer who was checking to see if it was dead. It wasn't and it flicked its tail giving its captor a hefty thump.

The Norwegians were notable Basking Shark hunters and had dedicated shark fishing fleets, as they did for whaling. Average catch records showed a three-to-one

Dorsal fin. UK Basking Sharks now enjoy protection, but the fin trade is driving sharks to the brink of extinction in many places. © Colin Speedie 2005

A feeding shark. © Colin Speedie 2005

Breaching. Basking Sharks are often seen breaching, which is generally assumed to be associated with courtship and/or with attempts to get rid of parasites. © Colin Speedie 2006

ratio of females to males, a figure that was much higher in the case of Gavin Maxwell. From the 1950s, some Basking Sharks caught in British waters were used to supply the Far East fin trade and this continued into the 1970's, although they were also then coming from Ireland. It is fortunate that the methods of killing were not more efficient during the period in question, or the already mentioned figure of around 100,000 sharks killed in the 20th century would certainly be much higher.

Interestingly, the hunters knew their prey by different names. To Scottish fishermen the shark is known as Muldoan, meaning "sunfish" or "sailfish", the Gaelic name is Cearban and the Nordic name is Brugde. Ken Watterson, an Isle of Man based Basking Shark researcher working in the 1980/90's, called his first research boat Gobbag Vooar, which is Manx Gaelic for big mouth.

One of the best documented accounts of Basking Shark fishing is that of Gavin Maxwell's enterprise on Soay. Although best known for "Ring of Bright Water", Maxwell wrote several other books and his Harpoon at a Venture is the history of his time as a Hebridean shark fisherman. The book provides lots of valuable information about post-war British Basking Shark hunting and the sale of products derived from them. In 1945 Basking Shark oil was selling for £80 a tonne, and it was a rising market. By 1947, prices had increased to £110. An average shark would produce 358 kilos, which made each animal worth about £45 in oil. All these amounts were a great deal of money 60 years ago.

On one occasion Maxwell records trying to kill a shark using a Breda light machine gun, which he kept on board to deal with mines left over after the war. Maxwell's first kill was a female measuring eight metres overall, with a girth of more than five metres and a tail just under two metres across. The head was one-and-a-half metres from the nose tip to the first gill slit, and the dorsal fin just under one metre. A big fish by any standards but not as big as they get. Colin Speedie has seen two or three sharks he estimated to be nearly 12 metres long.

Maxwell acknowledges that he made two big mistakes in his venture. Firstly, he had to transport all the sharks back to his factory at Soay. That was expensive and hugely time consuming – a factory ship with the catching boats would have been the answer. Secondly, he dealt in too many products - liver oil, frozen flesh, salted flesh, liver residue, dried fins, bone manure etc - instead of just concentrating on the most valuable. The sharks he caught were towed back to Soay and positioned at the factory slipway, a railway leading from the sea to the cutting up area. The carcasses were floated on to a bogie truck moving on rails and hauled up the incline by a large steam winch. Once on the cutting floor, sharks would be skinned by workers wearing armoured gloves to protect them from the abrasive skin, and then their livers would be removed. They would then be cut up and pieces placed in barrels at the oil extraction plant. The fins were put in tanks for the extraction of glue liquor, whilst the flesh went into the ice house. Remains of Soay factory still exist (See page 41).

Watkins and Maxwell were competitors and often hunted in the same areas. In the four years that Maxwell caught Basking Sharks he killed seven females for every male, and recalls on several occasions seeing males with claspers (external sexual organs) about a metre long and 18cm thick. However as the researcher Ken Watterson observed lampreys normally attach themselves in the genital area and it is possible that on occasions lampreys were mistaken for claspers.

In 1946 a Chinese businessman wrote to Maxwell offering money for sharks' fins, pointing out the high value these could achieve due to their perceived aphrodisiac values. It's believed this could be one of the first instances of the fin trade coming to Britain. During Maxwell's time on Soay, the Sweeneys of County Mayo, on the West coast of Ireland, sent a representative to consult with him as they, too, were planning to establish a Basking Shark fishery. At the end of 1946 under-capitalisation caused Maxwell to sell out for £13,550. He became managing director of the new company and got a shareholding as part of the deal.

The need for having a factory ship was sharply brought home on one occasion in particular when, in two days, Maxwell's boats killed 15 sharks 70 miles from Soay. The time needed for ferrying them to the on-shore factory would have been prohibitive so he decided to beach them on the island of Scalpay. There, his men cut out the livers, putting them in herring barrels to transport them back to base. This method of working continued and a small steamer was hired to transport the barrels.

By the end of the 1947 season the company decided to use spotter planes and a factory ship was to begin operations the following year. However, neither plan actually materialised and Maxwell resigned in July 1948. In 1949, his successor put the company's assets up for sale. Maxwell's gunner Tex Geddes, bought some of the gear and continued as a freelance shark fisherman, enjoying moderate success.

The shark whose oil once lit the streets of Dublin and provided targets for the RAF to practise on is now under most threat in our waters from accidental "by-catch" in fixed fishing gear such as gill nets and lobster pot ropes, together with collisions with leisure craft users. Jet skiers, water skiers and boaters sometimes come into contact with Basking Sharks feeding at the surface, especially around headlands, and every year injuries are recorded. On occasions, the sharks are rammed deliberately but, in the main, the contact is accidental.

In August 1999 when I was on a day trip to Lundy Island off North Devon, our ferry narrowly missed a Basking Shark as we approached the jetty. Fins were visible all across the bay and we observed fins from the cliff tops in several places as we walked around the island. Cliff walkers in parts of Devon, Cornwall, the Isle of Man, and the Western Isles often have the opportunity of seeing these creatures. The Shark Trust offers a code of conduct series of guidelines to boat operators for observing the sharks while avoiding disturbing or endangering them.

Until recently, it was believed that their disappearance in the winter months indicated that Basking Sharks hibernated. In 2003 studies (Sims et al) disproved this theory and showed that, in fact, the sharks spent more time at depth of up to 900 metres feeding on deepwater plankton. Satellite tagging (Sims et al again) has shown that Basking Sharks move thousands of miles during the winter months tracking plankton blooms to feed.

Basking Sharks are now completely protected in British seas out to the 12-mile limit and the only humans hunting them are doing so for purposes of eco-tourism (See chapter 5). In 2002, the species received Appendix II listing from the Convention on International Trade in Endangered Species (CITES) and was listed on Appendix I of the Bonn Convention on Migratory Species (CMS) in 2005. In addition, there is a UK Biodiversity Action Plan for Basking Sharks.

The Killer Whale and the Great White Shark are both known to attack Basking Sharks but pose nothing like the threat that industrial fishing did. Colin Speedie hopes that numbers may slowly be starting to recover from the lows reached during the last century, when man hunted this gentle giant.

A new twist to shark eco-tourism. Cartoon Chris Wylie.

Chapter Five

SHARK ECO-TOURISM

In the 1970's Porbeagle fishing off Crackington Haven in North Cornwall was so prolific that boats used to queue to drift chum. Whenever I recall that situation, I think what a shame it was that those anglers were killing their catches, and not just observing them. With the numbers that used to exist then, cage diving would have been possible as long as the sharks cooperated and, if the sharks had been examined and admired rather than over fished, they would still be plentiful.

Annual catches of Blue Sharks by the Looe angling fleet were once 2000, 3000, 4000, 5000...even, in one year, 6000 and, although the number has now dropped to fewer than 200, there are still angling boats that pursue both Blues and Porbeagles on Cornwall's north and south coasts. In South Africa's Western Cape yesterday's fishermen and trophy anglers have become today's shark guardians and eco-tourism operators. So why can't the same mentality rule in Britain? Although vastly depleted, we've still got the sharks, and we've got the angling boats, so why couldn't we do the same? If cage diving were to prove possible it would be a win for the sharks, a win for the skippers, a win for holidaymakers and shark enthusiasts - and a win for eco-tourism!

In August 2005, my wife, Jacqui, and I decided to see if shark eco-tourism would work in the UK. Together with groups of volunteers, we ran two pilot days out of Looe, aware of the sceptical glances of skippers peering suspiciously and doubtingly at our chum slick. No floats, no baited hooks, just the usual chum bags over the side and another one with a float on a line 15 metres astern. The first shark arrived after 40 minutes and the second an hour-and-a-half later. A large two-and-a-half metre Blue Shark grabbed our bait bag and we had a tug of war. I lost, the bag ripped and our shark had breakfast, lunch and supper all in one go.

We steamed back to Looe and on the way I spotted and rescued a net-entangled porpoise. Two Blue Sharks, a number of dolphins, and a porpoise rescue - not a bad day. The following weekend we drew a blank but one out of two is 50 per cent, and we decided to take the idea further and run a proper pilot project in the summer of 2006 with three Blue Shark days out of Looe, and three Porbeagle days out of Bude and Padstow. We sent two press releases to the diving magazines which resulted in short, one paragraph items - and we also put the idea on our website. The response was phenomenal: the phone rang constantly and our email box filled up. Thereafter, we had to double our planned six days to 12 with six participants per day. All in all, around 2,000 people enquired after 72 places. There was no doubt that the interest was there!

The winter was spent planning and plotting. Two shark cages were built, and I designed a special "hook over the gunnels" dive platform and steps. Many enquirers questioned the necessity for cages for Blues and Porbeagles. However, both are predatory animals and while, as far as I know, there are no confirmed records of Porbeagle attacks, there are records of Blues being dangerous to humans so safety was a vital factor. Other considerations were how to provide stability in the water in Cornwall's four-six knot surface currents, and how to keep the sharks around the boats. In the past, I have deployed a rope line to hang onto, which, with a float on it tucked under an arm, provided hands-free anchorage but not total stability. Caging our participants not only provided total safety for both sharks and humans, but also solved the stability problem and enabled me to bait the animals safely right up to the cage.

I knew I could attract Blues to a cage (see page 49), or to a swimmer, but Porbeagles are shy and my two previous attempts to get into the water with them had failed. One of those attempts gained me a brief glimpse and the other was a washout, resulting in no sighting at all. A human finning around struggling to maintain position in a five-knot current is not going to result in calm sharks, and, generally, they are unlikely to hang around long after a snorkeller gets in the water. As soon as we started chumming, I planned to put the cage into the water so there would be no splash or disturbance when the sharks arrived. I hoped then to slip our observers into the cage, and keep the shark around it. Provided conditions were flat enough, it seemed cages would be the best way forward for all these reasons.

The 2006 pilot project went well and a great deal was learned. The success rate in encountering Blue sharks was 66 per cent on the north coast. In 2007, we expanded the project to more than 50 days, which meant we could take out more than 300 participants. As it happened, a summer of unsettled weather meant that we lost half our planned days but the encounter success rate remained at a similar level. In short, we had proved the concept worked and that a profitable eco-tourism opportunity was there to be developed. Shark angling skippers from Devon, Cornwall and South Wales are the logical people to take this forward. And, at the time of writing there is keen interest from them.

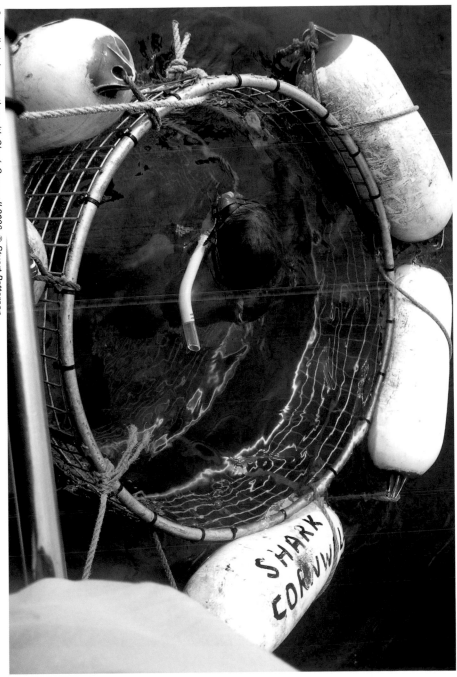

Our secret weapon, the mirrored chum tube. © *Tony Bennett*

A man's eye view of a Blue Shark cruising passed cage, Shark Cornwall 2006. © M. Boothman

Shark angling can also be classed as eco-tourism and opportunities to take part are many and diverse. In the southwest of England Looe, Padstow, Falmouth, Mevagissey, Bude, St Ives, Newquay, Penzance, Plymouth, Clovelly, Hartland and many other fishing harbours offer shark angling. In Pembrokeshire, Porbeagle and Blue Shark fishing is possible in at least three places. The Isle of Wight provides opportunities to encounter Thresher Sharks as do the Channel ports. Soupfin Shark (Tope) fishing is common all around the British Isles with many good spots in particular on the North Sea coast. The rugged and dramatic Pentland Firth is where the world record Porbeagle Shark was caught and the little port of Scrabster, next to Thursoe, has two boats that can be chartered for shark angling.

After angling, the largest and best established shark eco-tourism in British seas is Basking Shark watching. There are three hotspots for this activity and all offer good chances of sightings. However, the big difference between watching Basking Sharks and baiting sharks for cage diving is that with Basking Shark watching operators cannot create opportunities. The sharks are either on the surface and visible or they are not, and, if they are not, there is nothing anyone can do about it, whereas with baiting or chumming the operator has an element, a small element, of control or influence.

Cornwall, the Isle of Man and North West Scotland (the Sea of the Hebrides) are the three best locations in Britain for spotting Basking Sharks. Sometimes they can be seen from the shore but the best chance for success lies in going to sea armed with a pair of binoculars. Operators offering Basking Shark watching trips can easily be found in the three areas mentioned. Some offer viewing only from boats whereas others specialise in putting experienced people in the water to snorkel with these huge sharks. Typically, snorkellers will be dropped in the water near the sharks and the operators' boat will then move away to minimise disturbance, and negate the possibility of upsetting the sharks.

With the huge increase in public interest in marine wildlife in general and sharks in particular, shark eco-tourism in Britain is certain to expand. Eco-tourism has two enormous values to the cause of shark conservation. Firstly, it provides a great opportunity to increase public awareness of sharks in a balanced and positive way thereby promoting conservation values; and, secondly, live sharks can provide earning opportunities day after day whereas one that is dead only has a one-time value. The fact is that man will protect wildlife if there's money in it for him.

The following is the Cage Diving Code of Conduct that I wrote for the Shark Trust. It may give readers an insight into how this form of eco-tourism works, and provide a guide as to what to look for when selecting an operator.

CODE OF CONDUCT FOR CAGE DIVING OPERATORS

The term "cage diving" is a misnomer because diving itself is not involved. Participants enter a cage that, typically, will be no more than three metres in depth, and then go to the bottom of it for viewing. Snorkelling, breathholding, and air lines from scuba tanks are used and in all cases, the participant's head is less than a metre below the surface.

This code of conduct is not intended as a comprehensive set of safety rules but is to promote good practice in interaction with sharks. At the time of writing, shark cage diving (as described) takes place in countries that include South Africa (Great White Sharks), Isla Guadeloupe (Great White Sharks), South Australia (Great White Sharks), Cornwall (Blue Sharks), Bermuda, the Caribbean and South Africa (Tiger Sharks).

GOOD PRACTICE.

1. Legal (dependent on local laws) products only should be used in shark chumming
2. Cages should be robust enough to withstand mouthing or accidental bumping by the sharks (Great White Sharks)
3. Viewing ports should be large enough for good viewing and photography, but not large enough to permit entry of sharks into the cage
4. Sharks should not be fed as there is evidence that this can lead to "conditioned" behaviour
5. Sharks should not be allowed to bite baits, bait tubes or chum sacks
6. Sharks should not be teased or worked into a frenzy so that they behave like circus animals
7. Sharks should not be touched or handled by operators - eg, Great White Sharks are often baited to the side of boats, and then teased into putting their heads out of the water so that operators can grab their noses prior to pushing them back into the water
8. Sharks should not be touched or handled by those in cages
9. When drawing baits towards cages to bring sharks close to participants, care should be taken not to make them charge after the bait thereby producing the risk of crashing into or colliding with the cage possibly resulting in injury to the sharks and/or the participants
10. Baits should be kept away from propellers and other sharp objects to avoid injuries to sharks
11. Participants should be advised at the start of the trip that calm surface conditions are necessary for safe cage entry/exit, and that, in the event of it not being possible to deploy the cage, participants will not be able to get into the water but will be restricted to watching the sharks from the deck
12. Closed-top cages must be capable of easy, quick opening from inside
13. Participants should never be allowed to wear their own wetsuits. If they insist then operators should ensure they are thoroughly washed after the dive. (Clearly it would not be a good idea for people on holiday to be cage diving one day in their own wetsuit and get it thoroughly impregnated with the smell of chum, and then to go surfing the next day in areas where there are sharks that might endanger them)

14. Operators must allow for the direction of their chum slicks in terms of influence on non-related activities. For example, drawing inshore sharks out to sea away from bathers is obviously safe. However, a chum slick going across a bathing beach could bring sharks into contact with bathers
15. Being in contact with the public gives operators the opportunity to promote shark conservation to their clients. It is urged that education and conservation be made part of the cage diving experience.

Below is a list of operators working at the time of writing. It is not complete and I apologise to anyone I have left out.

Location Activity Operator/Contact.

Looe, Cornwall. Shark Angling - Shark Angling Club
Padstow, Cornwall. Shark Angling - Padstow Angling Centre
Bude, Cornwall. Cage diving – Shark Cornwall
Penzance, Cornwall. Basking Shark Watching - Marine Discovery
Penzance, Cornwall. Basking Shark Watching - Elemental Tours
Newquay, Cornwall. Basking Shark Watching – Atlantic Divers
Newquay, Cornwall. Cage diving – Atlantic Divers
Bude, Cornwall. Cage diving – Bude Boat Charter
St. Keverne, Cornwall. Basking Shark Watching - Porthkerris Divers
St Keverne, Cornwall. Basking Shark Watching - Dive Action
Bude, Cornwall. Shark Angling - Bude Boat Charter
Peel, Isle of Man. Basking Shark Watching - Various
Pembroke Docks, Milford Haven. Shark Angling - Various
Scrabster, near Thursoe, Scotland. Porbeagle Angling - Various

I have not included websites and other contact points because this is not intended to be a directory. It is merely to provide guidance as to where to start looking.

The South African model shows how economically important shark eco-tourism can be. In January 2008 my friend Craig Ferreira in South Africa told me that the twelve cage diving operators were generating over 70 million rand (£5, 400,000) per year i.e. approximately £450,000 per operator. This is the direct revenue being taken by the operators, the value of the industry is much larger once all the tangential aspects have been considered. Hotel rooms, shuttle buses, restaurants, airlines, retailers, and a host of others benefit directly from tourists coming to South Africa to see sharks. We can do some similar figures for Cornwall. In 2007 we had over 300 clients booked for cage diving at £95 per head. This is £28,500 of direct revenue and can be doubled if one assumes that each person spent another £100 in the county. We did only four days a week with six people a day, so on this basis it's easy to see how one operator working seven days a week, and taking out eight to ten clients daily would comfortably produce over £100,000 a year for himself and other benefiting businesses. I believe Cornwall could easily support ten operators which would mean a million pounds in revenue from cage diving; this figure would greatly increase were Basking Shark watching revenue added. The Shark Angling Club based in Looe, Cornwall now operates 8 shark angling boats and another 3 work independently, and for the last fifty-three years shark angling has been a major contributor to Looe's economy.

You can only kill something once, so dead value is one time, whereas live value is a day after day income stream. I am a cynic and believe that mankind is such an awful out of control species that unless it's in his interest not to do so he will end up killing most wildlife. Money is a great incentive not to kill, it's simple "if it pays it stays" that's why we have to develop shark eco-tourism and give sharks a real live value.

Chapter Six

BLUES, TOPE, ANGELS, HOUNDS, DOGS AND CATS

(Blue Sharks, Soupfin Sharks (Tope), Angel Sharks, Smoothhounds, Starry Smoothhounds, Spiny Dogfish (Spurdog), Nursehounds, Small Spotted Catsharks).

THE BLUE SHARK (Prionace glauca)

The first time I saw a Blue Shark was in the 1960s, while angling off Looe in South Cornwall. In those days, shark anglers killed what they caught, and they could not have foreseen the tragic collapse in shark populations that has occurred since. As I have said, angling has barely contributed to this position. Nevertheless, I am sure that those who killed what they caught now look back with regret.

The Blue Shark is probably the most wide ranging shark seen in British waters. Animals tagged off Cornwall and southern Ireland have often later been identified on the eastern seaboard of the United States, and those tagged in the North Atlantic have been recaptured in the South Atlantic. Blue Sharks are truly oceanic nomads and tagging programmes have helped establish the amazing journeys they undertake. It appears that mating occurs mostly on the western side of the Atlantic and the males largely remain there while the females set off on an ocean crossing. Whether all impregnated females make this journey has not been established but all the evidence points to them getting impregnated in the western Atlantic and then pupping on the eastern side. My own observations off Cornwall certainly bear this out as all the larger sharks I come across are females together with a lot of juveniles. I have on more than one occasion heard of rod-and-line caught pregnant females pupping on deck and all the baby sharks, together with mother, being quickly returned to the water and swimming off satisfactorily.

After copulation, males and females go their separate ways. The females store the sperm in their shell glands, and then self-fertilise several months later. However, the circular, round-trip migration route is not undertaken by all Blue Sharks all the time, and the picture is complicated by a degree of north-south migration. This involves sharks of both sexes and all ages and sizes.

As more tagging is carried out and more data becomes available, it is evident that Blue Shark movement patterns in the Atlantic are highly complex. North Atlantic Blue Sharks don't necessarily remain north of the equator: a shark tagged off Salcombe in Devon was recaptured three years later in the South Atlantic not far from the bulge of Brazil. Scientists don't have conclusive evidence as to how Blue Sharks navigate. However, experiments have shown that they can sense the earth's magnetic field and indications are that somehow, this ability may be used to chart their courses. Blue Sharks are mainly nocturnal feeders and tend to hunt in deeper waters. Herring, hake, bluefish and mackerel are all regular prey for western Atlantic dwelling sharks, and squid, octopus, cod, smaller sharks, pollock, and haddock are on the menu on the British side of the ocean. They will scavenge and floating whale carcasses in particular get their attention.

The vision that comes to most minds on hearing the word shark is that of a Great White, which is many people's favourite and their idea of the perfect shark. For me, though, two "British species" are real "sharky" sharks. The enigmatic, stout, powerful "Great White like" Porbeagle is a challenging and captivating creature, and the electric blue, slim, sleek almost serpentine Blue Shark is an equal favourite (see page 62).

The Blue Shark is also called the Great Blue and on the rare occasions I have seen specimens larger than three metres, it was easy to see why. I have swum with these sharks off Cornwall, in the Mediterranean, and off South Africa and California. They may not be as menacing as Great Whites, Tiger or Bull Sharks but they must be respected as potentially dangerous. I once had one grab my fin and while it let go quickly and I thought it was funny at the time, I later realised the shark didn't know that my fin wasn't my ankle, which would not have been funny.

In baited situations, the shark is responding to the "ringing of the dinner bell" and it can certainly present threats. This was clearly illustrated on the last day of 2007, when I spent a magical few hours chumming for sharks off Cape Point with my friends Chris and Monique Fallows. By the end of a four-hour period, we had attracted more than 20 Blue Sharks, over 10 Makos, and a large (more than three metres) brown Shark, which was either a Dusky Shark or a Bronze Whaler. There was enough bait and chum in the water to promote very excited behaviour and small Blue Sharks were behaving aggressively, competing for food with much larger Makos and showing no fear at all. The degree of excited, aggressive and competitive behaviour caused us to cease our activities before any sharks got hurt or damaged by colliding with the dive platform or a propeller. The experience graphically illustrated two points. Shipwreck victims injured, bleeding and

Five Blues at once. It doesn't get much better than this! © Richard Peirce

Blue Shark. © Chris Fallows

Smallspotted Catshark. © *Sally Sharrock*

Angel Shark. © *Simon Rogerson*

The almost serpentine Blue Shark. © *Richard Peirce*

struggling in the water could be in serious trouble in the presence of Blue Sharks, and eco-tourist operators working in chummed situations should know what they are doing, and err on the side of caution when making decisions.

The Blue Shark must keep moving. It has large pectoral fins that act like wings, the liver acts as a buoyancy device, and a powerful tail with a large upper lobe works as the propulsion unit keeping the shark in motion. Tests compared the efficiency of a 2.1 metre Blue Shark to that of a submarine, and, on a weight comparison basis, the shark required six times less propulsive power. These sharks are fast and have been recorded achieving speeds of up to 39.5 kph and travelling 71 kilometres in a day.

Due to the massive migrations Blue Sharks undertake and their dispersal throughout most of the world's oceans, they are probably the most fished shark species. Also, instead of several separate populations being exploited by different fisheries, we now suspect that the north Atlantic gathering is just one population involved in a complex series of migration patterns and being depleted by fisheries on every route.

THE SOUPFIN SHARK (TOPE) (Galeorhinus galeus)

I don't know why but the word Tope sounds a little dull and doesn't really conjure up an image of a shark. Soupfin Shark not only sounds better but also the use of this name is a continual reminder of why sharks are being killed all around the world in unsustainable numbers, hence my use of this less common name.

The fish is also known as the School Shark, Vitamin Shark and the Oil Shark. The Soupfin Shark is caught on rod and line around most of the British coast. Fishing history was made in May 2002, when an albino Soupfin Shark was caught more than 129 kilometres from the Cornish coast. Albino Sharks are extremely rare and so there was great excitement when this ghostly looking creature turned up in a trawl.

As with the Blue Shark, tagging programmes have established that the Soupfin Shark is a long distance traveller. The UK Shark Tagging Programme and others have produced solid evidence of the extent of their movements. Soupfin Sharks tagged in the English Channel, Irish Sea, and off Scotland's west coast have been recaptured off Spain, Portugal and Morocco, the Azores and the Canary Islands. One Soupfin Shark was known to have travelled more than 1770 kilometres in 62 days. Tagging results also seem to indicate that female sharks head south for warmer water pupping sites while males remain in northerly waters. Soupfin Sharks mainly live close to the seabed and have been recorded in depths of up to 400 metres. They are opportunistic feeders whose diet consists of bony fish and invertebrates, and they often find themselves part of the diet of larger sharks.

Soupfin Sharks are thought to have pups every two or three years with litter sizes of up to 50. As one of their names makes clear, they are often found in schools, which makes them vulnerable to fishing and angling. Tagging has also helped to establish that Soupfin Sharks are long living and probably attain ages of up to 60 years old.

This beautiful, slender, grey brown shark is fished all over the world for its liver oil, meat and fins, which has resulted in many populations being seriously depleted.

ANGEL SHARK (Squatina squatina)

The Angel Shark is not most people's idea of a shark. It is a large, stocky, flat fish that wouldn't win any beauty contests judged by those thinking of shapes more commonly associated with sharks. It can reach lengths of approaching two-and-a-half metres and has a grey to reddish brown dotted and spotted topside. This "ambush predator" spends most of its day lying buried on the seabed with its eyes protruding. It moves off the bottom at night and is a strong swimmer. The upper skin surface of the Angel Shark is covered with spiky-shaped dermal denticles (tiny, tooth-like structures), whereas the underside has flattened scale-like denticles, which protect it as it swims over obstacles on the seabed. It is also one of those sharks capable of pumping water over its gills without swimming.

This species is severely depleted in much of its range however in March 2008 it finally received protection out to six nautical miles under the Wildlife and Countryside Act. This applies only to English waters and similar protection is being lobbied for, in Scotland, Wales and Northeren Ireland. In December 2006 the Angel Shark was declared locally extinct in the North Sea by ICES (the International Council for the Exploration of the Seas). Also sometimes known as Monkfish, this shark produces up to 25 pups following an eight to 10 month gestation period, and pupping in British seas usually occurs in mid summer. There is a record of its usual diet of flat fish, skates, crustaceans, and molluscs, having at least once been augmented by a cormorant!

SMOOTHHOUND and STARRY SMOOTHHOUND (Mustelus mustelus, Mustelus asterias)

The Smoothhound Shark is a favourite of aquaria and is found all round Britain's shores. It spends most of its time on the bottom but is also found mid-water. It feeds primarily on crustaceans and has crushing teeth adapted for this diet. However, bony fish, and cephalopods are also on its diet sheet.

The Starry Smoothhound is another favourite for keeping in captivity, where, with good husbandry, it does quite well and has been known to breed. Reaching nearly the same size as the Smoothhound (1.4 – 1.6 metres/4 ft 6 ins – 5 ft) this shark is distinguishable from its near namesake by lots of small white dots and spots on its back and sides.

The Starry Smoothhound is slightly more particular over its eating and is thought to exist on a diet made up entirely of crustaceans. Also, like the Smoothhound, it is under no targeted pressure from fishing but is taken as by-catch.

SPINY DOGFISH (Squalus acanthias)

The Spiny Dogfish is also known as the Spurdog, Piked Dogfish, the Doggy, and, to many fish and chip shop customers, as Rock Salmon. This slender shark can reach sizes of up to two metres and is listed by the International Union for the Conservation of Nature (IUCN) as "endangered" in British seas. I always think the nickname "dogfish" is a slightly unfair way of describing this nearly two metre bluish grey shark; "dogfish" certainly doesn't have the same ring to it as "shark" does!

The Spurdog is found almost all over the world and was once probably the most abundant species. Like the Smoothhound and Starry Smoothhound, it is an aquarium favourite, and it is also targeted by sports anglers. Some Spurdogs undertake north-south migrations and others are resident all-year-round. It is thought that the species is depleted in British waters by 95 per cent or more, and effective protection is being urgently sought by the Shark Trust and others.

The Spurdog is extremely long living and may reach 100. However, its late maturity, between 10 and 25 years-old, added to its habit of schooling, makes it particularly vulnerable to fisheries. I earnestly hope that the Spurdog doesn't join the Angel Shark in being declared extinct in some British seas.

NURSEHOUND and SMALLSPOTTED CATSHARK (Scyliorhinus stellaris, Scyliorhinus canicula)

The Nursehound Shark is also known as the Bullhuss and the Huss and while the name doesn't sound very sharky this 1.5 metre (4 ft 6 ins) shark is a handsome creature. Large spots and dots cover a creamy golden brown topside. The Nursehound inhabits waters all round Britain's coasts and egg cases or mermaids' purses found washed up on the shore may have contained baby Nursehounds that take around nine months to hatch. This shark has no real commercial value and so is not targeted by fisheries. Nevertheless, the Nursehound is on the IUCN Red List as "near threatened". It eats cephalopods, crustaceans, molluscs, bony fish and small sharks.

Confusingly, the really pretty little Blackmouth Catshark is also known as the Lesser Spotted Dogfish. Reaching lengths of up to 50 cms this is our smallest commonly sighted shark. Like the Spurdog, the Smoothhound and the Starry Smoothhound, it is a favourite among aquaria, where it does really well and frequently breeds in captivity. Often taken as by-catch in fisheries, the Smallspotted Catshark has a high survival rate when discarded and returned to the sea. Of all our sharks, this species is possibly the least threatened and the population is thought to be stable. Crustaceans, gastropods, small bottom invertebrates, worms and fish are all on its menu.

Chapter Seven

WARM BLOODED HUNTERS – THE BIG THREE: MAKOS, PORBEAGLES AND THRESHERS

SHORTFIN MAKO (Isurus Oxyrinchus)

Highly valued by anglers, the Mako is the fastest shark, a real fighter and, some say, the most intelligent.

There are records of Makos in all British seas but in recent years there have been few confirmed sightings. If we take West of England shark fishing activity from Dorset round the peninsula to Somerset, I would estimate that more than 100 angling boats chum for sharks each summer. Over a three-month period each year that's a lot of water covered by a lot of chum, and, if Makos were there, we would be hearing of encounters. Canadian research for the western side of the Atlantic shows the Mako to be seriously depleted, and anecdotal evidence from British seas indicate the same.

The record for a Mako caught in British waters is held by Mrs. J Yallop for a shark caught on May 12th 1971. It weighed 227 kgs (500 lbs). (See page 26)

Like its cousin the Porbeagle, the Mako – whose name is derived from the Maori for shark - is good to eat and it is this, together with its noted fighting abilities, that make it the most prized of sharks by big game anglers. Makos breach (jump) when caught on rod and line. Indeed, a series of athletic leaps is common. The Shortfin Mako has long been a recognised species in British waters, unlike the Longfin Mako. Cornish angling skippers believe the Mako is the most intelligent shark and, while this opinion is based on anecdotal evidence, it is a fact that the Mako does have the biggest brain of any shark relative to its body weight.

Craig Thorburn carried out interesting work with Makos in New Zealand. This showed that they learnt to associate some shapes with food. Thorburn's experiments involved black circles and squares. The squares yielded a model fish as a reward while the circles resulted in real fish. The Makos quickly learned to differentiate.

Further work with protective electric fields showed that Makos circled at the edge if they could see a potential meal inside the field. With other sharks the response was to flee to escape the electric field, whereas the Makos' brain overrode this tendency having received the visual information.

Like its cousins, Porbeagles and Great Whites, Makos have equal tails, which means that the upper and lower lobes are of similar size. Also, like the other two, Makos maintain a body temperature higher than that of the surrounding water.

Some shark species have fascinating migratory stories to tell and the Mako is one of them. It is present throughout the world's temperate and tropical seas. However, an American tagging programme revealed that the Mako has a strong preference for water temperatures in the range 17–22 C, and this factor largely determines its travel patterns.

In 1978, Frank Carey attached sonic transmitters to a shark caught off Cape Canaveral. The animal was tracked across the Gulf Stream to an area approximately 100 miles north of the Bahamas. The tag indicated that it had spent most of its time in the thermal corridor it favoured - i.e, 17–22 C. British waters rarely reach summer highs of much above 17 degrees so, in that sense, our seas are at the lower edge of the Mako's apparent preference.

The first evidence that Makos undertake transatlantic travel began to emerge in the late 1970's/early 1980's, when sharks tagged in the Western Atlantic regularly turned up as recaptures on the eastern side. One tagged in the Gulf of Maine was recaptured in mid-ocean 500 miles west of the Azores. In 1984 another tagged off Nantucket was recaptured nine months later to the west of Lisbon. Then, in 1992, one was caught off Madeira, having been tagged 11 months earlier 1,600 miles west at Flemish Cap. It appears that they may follow a North Atlantic migration route broadly similar to that of Blue Sharks.

Makos are generally assumed to be fish eaters and this was largely confirmed by a study carried out between 1972 and 1978, when 237 had their stomach contents analysed. Blue fish, tuna and mackerel were the most common remains identified. Squid - a common prey for Makos hunting in deeper water – together with cod and silver hake were also present. Eye witness accounts from around Britain tell of Makos preying on small seals, and a specimen from the Indian Ocean was found to have two turtle heads in its stomach. There are many accounts of clashes between Makos and Swordfish and it is not uncommon to find Makos washed up dead on beaches with Swordfish bills imbedded in them. A large female caught off

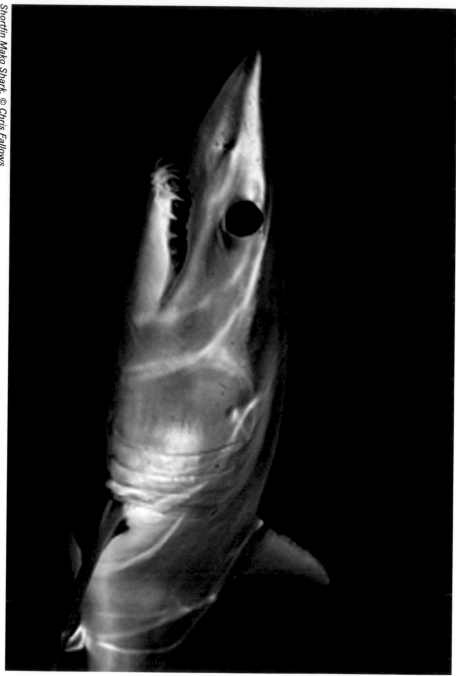

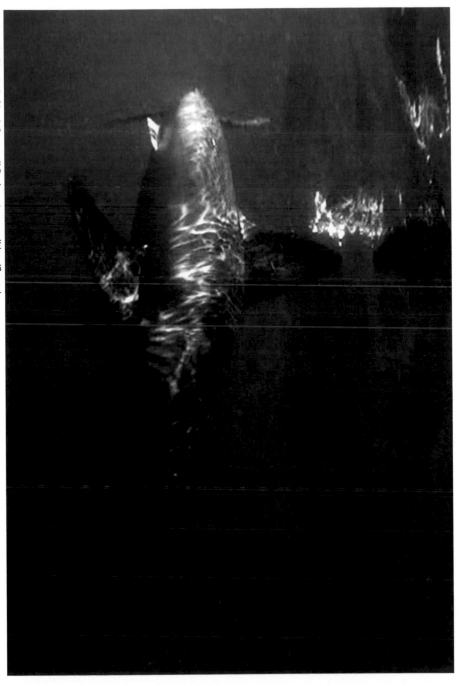

Porbeagle Shark. © Shark Cornwall Porbeagle expedition (Allen)

November 2007. 510kg (1122lbs) 5 metre world record Thresher Shark caught off Lands End.
© Rory Goodall

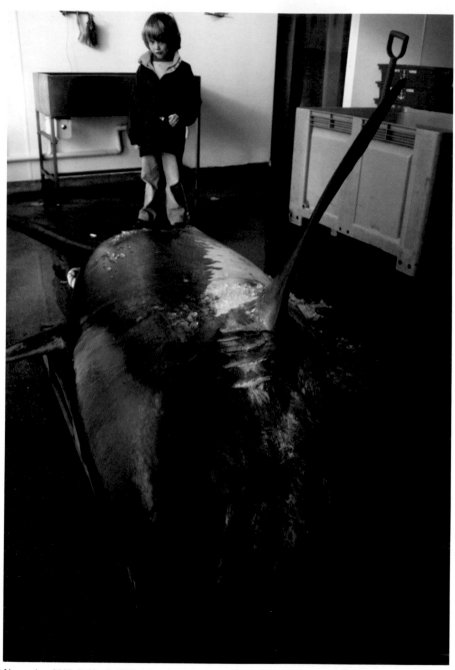

November 2007. 510kg (1122lbs) 5metre world record Thresher Shark caught off Lands End.
© Rory Goodall

Montauk in 1977 was found to have a 36-kilo piece of Swordfish in her stomach. The likely size of the whole Swordfish would have been between 180 and 220 kilos.

Makos commonly produce 10 to 15 pups, which are fully developed at birth and are currently listed on the IUCN (World Conservation Union) Red List as "near threatened". Females are known to achieve more than four metres in length, while males usually stop short of three metres.

While they are listed as dangerous and may attack if provoked, the International Shark Attack File records only 45 Mako attacks in the whole world since records began.

THE PORBEAGLE SHARK (Lamna Nasus)

Sitting at my desk in my office in Bude, North Cornwall, I look straight out to sea. Through my window I can see the place that we catch and tag Porbeagle Sharks. It may come across in this chapter that I look at Porbeagles in an almost proprietorial manner. That is because I regard them as my friends and I am proud that I have contributed to raising public awareness about these amazing creatures and the threats they face.

I started cage diving with Blue Sharks as a tourist activity in Britain in the summer of 2006. By the time this book is published, we will be preparing for summer 2008 and our first attempts at Porbeagle eco-tourism. These are very different sharks to try to attract to cages or to get into the water with. They are fast and wary. Those who have cage dived with Blue or Great White sharks will have noticed the relaxed, almost laid back way, those sharks cruise around the cages. There is nothing relaxed or laid back about Porbeagles. They are swift and dart in and out from the object that has interested them. Close interaction is difficult to engineer; they simply don't like being too close to humans in the water.

The Porbeagle is not a shark that we know a great deal about, so between 14 and 20 July in the summer of 2007 I ran the first ever Porbeagle shark expedition in UK waters, aided by seven volunteers. The aims of the expedition were:

- To be the first to deploy satellite (pop-off) tags on Porbeagles this side of the Atlantic
- To achieve the first decent quality underwater footage and still images of Porbeagles
- To observe the sharks on the surface and work out how to be able to get cage divers into the water with them

Four of the five satellite tags to be deployed were supplied by Nick Pade, a PhD student at Aberdeen University doing his thesis on Porbeagles. I provided the fifth tag.

The precise locations we worked have not been published because the sharks would be an easy target for commercial fishermen. Such fears were well founded because the week after our expedition we got reports of a longliner working around Lundy having caught and killed more than 60 sharks, we later discovered the number was closer to 90. During our five days we observed a sex bias towards females of probably 70 per cent. So the catching of more than 60 sharks, mostly females, will have had a devastating effect.

I knew that obtaining underwater images, both still and moving, would be difficult due to the Porbeagles' nervousness. Twice previously I had Porbeagles around my RIB in chummed situations and tried to slip into the water to get shots. On one occasion, I dropped into the water on the opposite side of the boat to the shark, but, by the time I had sneaked round the back hoping for a shot, it was gone. On the other occasion I repeated the tactic with only slightly more success. The shark did a fast, crossing pass angling towards me but jinked away just as I was thinking a shot might be possible. Therefore, I reckoned that the best chance of getting images lay in doing so by remote means. Simon Spear was the expedition's videographer and, using a polecam, assisted by Mike Sharland and David Green with a back-up camera, he obtained good footage on day one. We had five different sharks round our boat that day and, as soon as we had one in the chummed area, it would find the bait tube. Thereafter, I would work the shark towards the boat by using the tube. This was how we got the sharks close to the polecam for the movie images and from that footage we ran off still images.

The original plan was to catch sharks for tagging at the beginning of the expedition and then move on to the more difficult task of photography. As it turned out, the difficult part was achieved first! During the next four days we deployed four out of five of our satellite tags, three return tags, and took fin tips for DNA analysis. One tag was set for 30 days, two tags for 60 days, and the other for 90 days. The 30-day tag popped up on time 67 kilometres away off Newquay, the second 60-day tag surfaced near Lundy and the third, 170 kilometres south west off Land's End. The fourth, the 90-day tag re-surfaced 200 kilometres west of Ireland heading out into the Atlantic.

It's rare that you get to tick all the boxes. We deployed our tags, got our images, collected DNA and, during the video and photographic part of the week, I had an excellent opportunity to study the sharks free swimming near the boat.

From what I had observed cage diving was a problem well worth attempting to crack because these sharks would be really exciting to view. They are reactive to chum. At one time, I thought they were darting in and buzzing the pole camera, and then I realised the camera was right beside the chum bag. The mirrored bait tube had proved a very successful tool with Blue Sharks and so it was with Porbeagles. They never tried to grab it but always checked it out giving me confidence that we could use it to work them up to a cage. As stated in Chapter 5, the main reason for caging is to keep all humans involved under control in one place. Deploying the cage over the side from the time of arrival and at the start of chumming would mean that the sharks approached seeing the cage as part of the boat's profile.

Porbeagles school (or form aggregations), which makes them very vulnerable to over angling or over exploitation by commercial fishing. There are many examples of this. One occurred in December 2003, when Newlyn-based fisherman Martin Ellis caught and killed more than 130 Porbeagles in a week off South Cornwall. As already stated, another occurred a week after the end of our expedition, when a Bideford-based longliner caught 60 - 90 sharks in a single day near Lundy Island, which is 12 miles across the water from where we were working.

Our chumming activities had produced, perhaps, as many as 10 sharks around the boat at one time, so this was first-hand experience of how easy they would be to catch in large numbers once they had formed groups.

Research from the Western Atlantic indicates that Porbeagles often hunt together in loose groups of 20 or more. It is not established that Porbeagles hunt cooperatively but in his book "The Private Lives of Sharks" Michael Bright describes occasions when small groups of Porbeagles have been seen to herd prey into tight balls, with each shark taking its turn to charge into the ball and feed.

Like the Mako, the Porbeagle is warm-blooded, which enables fast pursuit of prey, mackerel, tope, dogfish, squid, cod, herring, hake, haddock and others are all on the menu. I am not aware of any hard evidence of Porbeagles taking mammalian flesh, but have heard claims from Cornish and Scottish fishermen that small seals and cetaceans (porpoises, dolphins) are also part of their diet. Certainly, they are opportunistic feeders and I can see no reason why a small, sick seal pup, porpoise or dolphin would be passed up as a potential meal.

The world angling record - a 230 kgs (507 lbs) Porbeagle was caught in British waters in 1993 in the Pentland Firth by Chris Bennett. In common with most of the other really large Porbeagles caught around Britain, it was a female. I have encountered several females of more than 200 kilos and up to three metres in length, but have only ever seen one male specimen that approached the 200-kilo mark.

THE THRESHER SHARK (Alopias Vulpinus)

On 27 September 2007, I received a text message from Phil Britts on board his boat, the Blue Fox, fishing near Trevose Head, in Cornwall, saying that he had just seen a four-to-four-and-a-half metre Thresher swimming near him. I have never seen a live Thresher in British waters, so I was immediately envious. The only Thresher I have seen in the UK was a dead female awaiting auction in Looe fish market in 2002. Truly a sad fate for a once magnificent animal.

Two months later (21st November) I received another call about an even larger shark, which, in fact, turned out to be a world record. This female Thresher was caught by accident by Roger Nowell while fishing for squid off Land's End. This giant weighing a colossal 510 kilos measured five metres in the body, and around 10 metres when the length of the upper caudal (tail) fin was added. It got caught in the boat's nets and, despite being alive, it was not judged possible for it to be released and to survive. Roger explained: "We'd only been out a few minutes and we bought the net up to have a look. There was no squid but this massive shark – it was the biggest one I'd ever seen. It was fairly alarming. It was still alive but had almost drowned in the nets and, as soon as it landed on deck, it thrashed around like crazy. It caused around £500 worth of damage to the hydraulics, it was that heavy."

I asked my friend and colleague Rory Goodall, of Penzance, to get me pictures of the shark for this book. (See pages 73-74) Later, this magnificent creature made a pitiful £0.23p per half kilo when sold at auction at Newlyn fish market. Prior to the world record referred to above the largest Thresher previously recorded was a specimen caught off New Zealand in 1981, which weighed 363 kilos - just the difference in weight between the two is the size of a large shark.

The Thresher is not uncommon in British waters. In August 2003, David Bailey caught a 110-kilo specimen off the Dorset coast. In November 2002 a 236-kilo male was caught near Looe, and in the summer of 2007 another large shark of approximately 363 kilos was reported to have been landed in Yorkshire.

Danny Vokins is a well known Isle of Wight-based shark angler. Down the years he has caught Blues, Porbeagles and now his main target species is the Thresher. The British record rod-and-line-caught Thresher is a 146-kilo specimen caught off Gosport by Steve Mills. In 2007, Danny caught one he estimated at more than 227 kilos. But, as Danny tags and releases all his sharks, his potential record was released and swam away.

I have never been sure what constitutes a shark attack because there are variations in the way the word "attack" is used. Bumps or nudges can count as "attacks" to some but in my book they don't. Danny Vokins and Ross Staplehurst felt "attacked" in June 1981, when at 2.00 pm a 181-kilo Thresher jumped into their boat, the incident making headlines around the world. Danny and Ross were saddened that, together with the others on board, they couldn't lift the large shark to get it back overboard and into the sea. They had to kill it and take it back to shore.

Threshers have been caught around the Isle of Wight in small numbers for as long as Danny can remember. In 2002, however, the numbers rose and for the past six years an average of 20 sharks a season have been caught, compared to the threes and fours of previous years. In recent years there have been reliable accounts of Threshers appearing all round the British Isles. They are distinguished by having huge tails that are almost the same length as their bodies. In nature, everything exists for a reason and so the Thresher's giant tail must serve a purpose. But, so far, science has not provided a conclusive answer, although it is generally agreed that the tail is a part, probably the major part, of the Thresher's hunting armoury.

Also known as the Thrasher, Fox Tail, Fox Shark, Whip Tail and Swivel Tail, the Thresher's names probably come from the many stories of sharks using their tails to secure prey. Accounts of the tail being used to disable fish, thrashing and stunning them, and being used as a herding device to pack fish together prior to devouring them are legion. There are also stories of a man being decapitated by a Thresher's tail, and of seabirds being struck on the surface and then eaten. What is certain is that the Thresher's tail is a formidable weapon.

Of the three species of Thresher - the Pelagic Thresher, the Big Eye Thresher and the Thresher itself - only the latter is commonly found in British seas. Threshers produce litters of between two and six pups, which, like their warm-blooded cousins the Mako and the Porbeagle, feed in uteri off unfertilised eggs.

Finally, and regrettably, the Thresher is on the IUCN Red List, is very vulnerable to fisheries and thought likely to be highly depleted.

Cartoon Chris Wylie.

Chapter Eight

SHARK ATTACK

Despite all popular perception, there has never been a "real" shark attack involving serious injury to humans in British waters. But the "Jaws" fear persists: razor sharp teeth tearing into human flesh while the victim thrashes helplessly around and the water turns red...etc! As I said at the beginning of Chapter I, I believe that sharks hit three basic human fear buttons: being eaten alive, the unknown, and not being in one's own element. Hippos kill many more humans each year than sharks do. But the thought of a "Hippo attack" doesn't send a shiver down the spine; unless, perhaps, at the time you happen to be in a small boat near a large, unhappy hippo!

So here are the facts:

In his book "Shark Attack" Mac McDiarmid mentions that in 1937 two sailing boats were attacked in Scottish waters possibly by the same shark, no further details are available. The most northerly shark attack recorded took place in British waters in June 1960. An 18-year-old German, Hans Joachim Schager, was taken to Bignold Hospital, Wick, Scotland, for treatment after being bitten on the arm. The "attack" had occurred 10 days earlier, when Schager was trying to take a small shark out of a net. The wound became septic and that was the reason he was taken to hospital. In August 1960 William Chapel was injured by an unidentified species of shark off Devon, when he was in the process of trying to land it. I do not count being injured by a shark when angling as an attack and these incidents are certainly not "unprovoked". I have many times been cut, bruised, and slapped by tails when tagging and releasing sharks. I regard these as accidents and anyway it was I who caused the accident by "attacking" the shark.

Trevor Housby in his book "Shark Fishing in British Waters" states that, until 1971, no definite attacks had been recorded in British seas. He then mentions two that took place within the space of four weeks, the first of which is also mentioned by

Mac McDiarmid in his book "Shark Attack", and involved a diver working his way out from the beach at Beesands in South Devon on 1 June of that year. The diver, Jimmy Johnson, had to fend off two attacks with a lobster hook before making his way back into water too shallow for the shark to follow, thus avoiding any possibility of a third attack. Housby states Johnson suffered nothing worse than shock. In his account, Housby suggests the shark was a Porbeagle.

I know no more than what was written by Housby and MacDiarmid but two questions come to mind. The first is what is meant in this case by "attack"? I have on many occasions had to push sharks away that, in the circumstances, I felt were too close, but I would not describe their passes or approaches as attacks. Secondly, the claimed identity of the shark is interesting in that approaching humans is unlikely Porbeagle behaviour. I have tried to get into the water with Porbeagles and they swim away quickly, so anxious are they to avoid human contact. An eye witness to the incident was certain that the shark was definitely attacking the diver, and both he and the diver agree the shark was around 3.6 metres long. This is longer than the world record Porbeagle, which casts further doubt on the shark having been of that species.

MacDiarmid writes that "the shark was believed to be a Mako (or possibly a Porbeagle)". The size estimate would more likely indicate a Mako and the International Shark Attack File (ISAF) lists a total of 45 Mako attacks on humans globally since records began but only three involving Porbeagles. The witness account agrees with that of Johnston and they are both clear that this was a real "attack". But was it unprovoked, or had Johnston or the circumstances surrounding him in some way provoked the shark? I would love answers to those questions because this seems to be the only genuine "in the water" shark attack in British seas thus far. The second attack mentioned by Housby occurred a couple of weeks later on the Kent coast, when a pair of large Threshers are alleged to have attacked a child swimming in shallow water. Housby feels this second attack was more of a chance meeting than a deliberate targeted attack. I agree.

As I mentioned in the previous chapter on Threshers, Danny Vokins and Ross Staplehurst got a shock when a Thresher Shark jumped into their boat. I suppose this could be classed as an attack because, in Danny's words, the shark had been stalking the boat for an hour before it decided to leap aboard. If we term this incident an attack it is only the second reliably witnessed attack/incident that I am aware of. However, those in the boat had been chumming for some time, which is certainly what attracted the shark. And I would not class any shark "attack" in a baited or chummed situation as unprovoked. So I believe this "incident", rather than "attack", was brought about by chumming. Luckily, no humans were hurt; the only loser was the shark, which paid with its life.

So let's examine the four potentially dangerous predatory sharks in our waters in terms of the possibility of an attack. They are the Blue Shark, the Mako, the Porbeagle, and the Thresher. According to the ISAF, there have been four recorded

Porbeagle attacks globally since records began. The figure for Makos is 45; for Blue Sharks, 38; and for Threshers, five. The ISAF lists two recorded shark attacks in British waters. The first (ISAF 2916 – 1971) is the Jimmy Johnson incident already recounted. The second is ISAF 2296 – 1996. This "attack" involved an unnamed oil rig diver in the Scot Field of the North Sea, who had the mounted light on his helmet "harassed" by a Porbeagle.

The big three in shark attack terms are the Great White (430 attacks); the Tiger Shark (145); and the Bull Shark (110). The Great White is recorded as being responsible for 63 human deaths, the Tiger for 28, and the Bull for 23. However, these figures must be treated with caution. As George Burgess of ISAF points out, positive identification of the attacking shark is unreliable because, naturally, victims are far more concerned with survival than with the identity of their attacker. Burgess also says that in attacks involving easily identified species such as the Great White, Tiger or Hammerhead, the shark is nearly always identified, while those involved in cases concerning the more-difficult-to-identify species seldom correctly identify the shark. There are those, and I am one of them, who believe that Great Whites are occasional, vagrant visitors to British waters. But there is no serious evidence, anecdotal or otherwise, of Bull Sharks ever being present - the temperature of British seas is outside their normal tolerance range. There have been claimed sightings of Tiger Sharks, but all, so far, unsubstantiated.

In practical terms, large sharks (those longer than 1.6 metres) can be considered a threat to humans, and it is clear that the two are coming together more often. I have watched the wet suit transform water use in Cornwall. There are now more people using the water and staying out longer all year around. If conditions are good, I can look out of my window in January and see several surfers riding the waves. In mid-winter British sea temperatures are still in the range known to be tolerated by Great White Sharks. Although shark populations are decreasing, human recreational use of the water is increasing, and where humans and sharks interact there is always the chance of an attack. However, even in areas well populated by dangerous sharks, attacks are rare and deaths even rarer. And Britain's inshore waters are not well populated by dangerous sharks so the chance of attack is remote. This is well illustrated by the fact that I have been able to find only one record of a witnessed "in the water" shark attack.

In conclusion the term "shark attack" means different things in different places. I believe a fair definition would be that a shark attack is an in the water incident, provoked or unprovoked, when a shark interacts with a human in an aggressive manner with the possibility of injury. Using this definition only one of the seven recorded "attacks" I have mentioned would be classed as a real attack. Of course shark attacks in British seas are possible but the chances remain remote and the risks tiny. In Chapter 10, "Strange & True", there are four genuine cases of injury being caused to humans by sharks in Great Britain on land. I have managed to find seven on or in the water incidents with two resulting in injury, and four inland incidents all resulting in injury. Based on these cases you are twice as likely in Britain to get injured by a shark on land as you are in the water!

Few creatures get the bad press that sharks continue to attract. Cartoon Chris Wylie.

Chapter Nine

MEDIA FEEDING FRENZIES

Much of what we think about any subject is based on our daily diet of information from the media. Of course, it is much more sensational for sharks to be portrayed as man-eating monsters than victims of over-fishing. The result is that the public is not just badly informed about sharks, it is often completely misled.

Why should it be front-page "news" that Mako Sharks have been seen off the Cornish coast? They have been there for tens of thousands of years. It's not news that a hippopotamus is spotted in a river in Zimbabwe, it's not news that a lion is seen in Kenya or an elephant is seen in India. It's not news because it's normal that they should be there. It's also normal that sharks should be observed in the sea. If a shark was spotted sitting on an aeroplane landing at Newquay Airport that would be news! A shark chasing sheep on Bodmin Moor would be news, but a shark in the sea - where do journalists expect them to be?

This largely pictorial chapter reproduces headlines, images and extracts from articles that have appeared in the UK national press over the last five years. I hope that by perusing them as a collection the reader will see what biased, unfair and unbalanced coverage sharks have received. However, perceptions are changing, and some parts of the media now produce balanced, factual coverage. Regrettably, though, many in the tabloid press continue down the "Jaws" road because that's what sells newspapers.

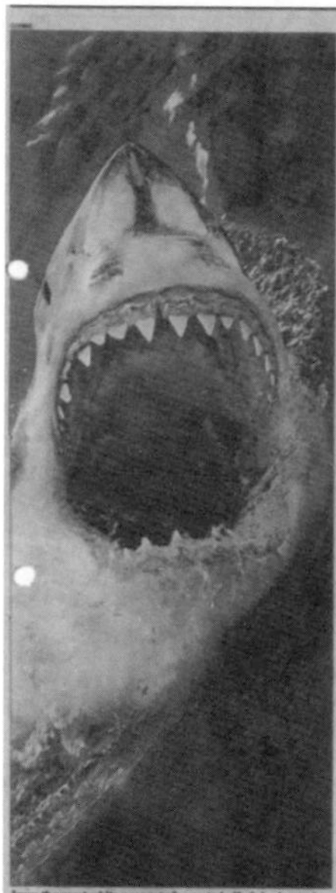

Jaws: the great white accounts for up to half of shark attacks

Four saved from death's jaws – by a pod of dolphins

By Roger Maynard
in Sydney
and Tosin Sulaiman

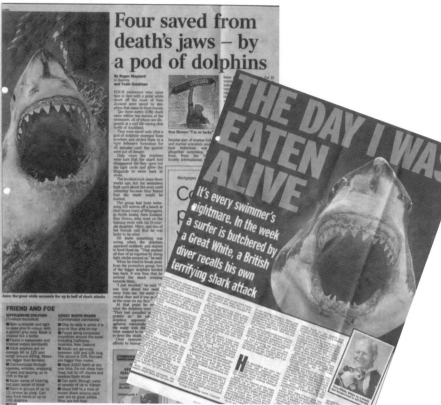

FOUR swimmers who came face to face with a great white shark off the coast of New Zealand were saved by dolphins that came to their rescue.

The three-metre (10ft) shark came within two metres of the swimmers, all of whom are lifeguards at a surf life-saving club north of Auckland.

They were saved only after a pod of dolphins emerged from nowhere and circled them in a tight defensive formation for 40 minutes until the quartet were out of danger.

Only when the dolphins were sure that the shark had disappeared did they open out the tight circle and allow the lifeguards to swim back to shore.

The incident took place three weeks ago, but the swimmers kept quiet about the story until yesterday because they feared that the shark would be hunted.

The group had been swimming 100 metres off a beach at their home town of Whangarei, in North Island, New Zealand. Ron Howes, who went on the training swim with his 15-year-old daughter, Niccy, and two of her friends said that he was lucky to be alive.

He knew something was wrong when the dolphins appeared suddenly and started to herd them up. "They pushed all four of us together by doing tight circles around us," he said.

When he tried to break away from the protective group, two of the bigger dolphins herded him back. It was then that he noticed the shark cruising towards them.

"I just recoiled," he said. "I was only about two metr... away from me, the water ... crystal clear and it was as c... as the nose on my face."

At that point he re... what the dolphins were... "They had corralled u... protect us," he sa... dolphins appeared ... agitated, repeatedly ... the water with the... what seemed to be ... to deter the shark.

Over centurie... affinity to huma...

Ron Howes: "I'm so lucky"

been ... years ... natu... be... hi... th...

became part of marine folk... and marine scientists said... their behaviour was ... altogether surprising. ... Rose, from the ... Society International, ...

FRIEND AND FOE

BOTTLENOSE DOLPHIN
(Tursiops truncatus)

- Skin is smooth and light to slate grey in colour, with a pinkish grey belly. Beak is shaped like a bottle
- Found in temperate and tropical waters worldwide
- Adult dolphins are on average 6ft to 12ft and weigh around 450kg. Males are bigger than females
- Communicate through squeaks, whistles, snapping of jaws and leaping up to 20ft in the air
- Acute sense of hearing, but poor sense of smell
- Swim in groups of up to 12, known as pods. Can also form herds of up to 100 dolphins

GREAT WHITE SHARK
(Carcharodon carcharias)

- Only its belly is white; it is grey or blue grey on top
- Found along temperate coastlines around the world including California, Australia, New Zealand
- Adults are generally between 10ft and 15ft long. The record is 22ft. Females are bigger than males
- Have 3,000 teeth at any one time. Do not chew their food, but rip off chunks and swallow them whole
- Can swim through water at speeds of up to 43mph
- About half to a third of known shark attacks each year are by great whites. Most are not fatal

THE DAY I WAS EATEN ALIVE

It's every swimmer's nightmare. In the week a surfer is butchered by a Great White, a British diver recalls his own terrifying shark attack

Bride's screams as her husband is eaten by shark

A great white shark: Common off the coast of South Australia

From **Richard Shears**
in Melbourne

A BRIDE on honeymoon watched in horror as her husband was torn to pieces by a great white shark.

Tina Bayes stayed on the beach while her husband Cameron, 26, paddled out to sea on his surfboard off the coast of South Australia.

As he turned round to wave at her the 12ft shark struck and dragged him under.

Other surfers said the shark initially appeared to release Mr Bayes, who somehow managed to get back on his board.

Seconds later, however, it grabbed him a second time and he was not seen again.

The shark then surfaced 500 yards from the beach, where it appeared to spit out a piece of surfboard.

With Mrs Bayes screaming from the shore, some of the other surfers paddled towards this area in search of her husband.

All they found was a pool of blood on the surface of the water.

The attack happened early yesterday off remote Cactus Beach, an area notorious for great whites.

Mr and Mrs Bayes, who were both New Zealanders, were on a working honeymoon in Australia.

Staying at campsites, Mr Bayes planned to earn money shearing sheep.

Surfer Jeff Hunter, who saw the attack, said: 'It was all very quick and very frightening.

'The shark had no hesitation. It took the surfer in a kind of circular motion.

'It looked horrendous,' Mr Hunter added. 'There was blood and surfboard everywhere.'

Mrs Bayes, who is also in her mid-twenties, was taken to hospital suffering from deep shock.

With no sign last night of her husband's body, a shark fisherman was called in to hunt down his killer over the next few days.

Great whites are common off Cactus Beach, which is reached from the famous highway which crosses the Nullabor Plain between Adelaide and Perth.

They feed off several seal colonies about two miles from shore and follow schools of salmon closer to shore.

Yesterday's attack was the first death of a surfer at the beach, although a local boy bled to death in 1975 after a great white shark bit off his leg while he was swimming.

Local surfboard maker Paul Gravelle said: 'Surfers are conscious of the risk of shark attack but we've always relied on the fact that there has never been a fatality here.'

Shark expert Rodney Fox, who needed more than 500 stitches after surviving an attack off the South Australian coast in 1963, said he would 'not feel comfortable' in the shark-infested waters of Cactus Beach.

'Unfortunately it's renowned as a great area to surf in,' he added.

'So you have this wonderful surfing area combined with one of the most dangerous stretches of water in the world.'

r.shears@dailymail.co.uk

JAWS II

Could there be MORE than one maneater off the Cornish coast?

By **Matthew Bayley**

IT is fast, ferocious and likes to sneak up on its prey.

Which means the mako shark does not make the most relaxing of swimming companions.

So the news that two have been spotted off Cornwall in just two weeks could leave some bathers preferring to stay on the shore.

Yesterday beaches across the region were on red alert after a fisherman reported seeing a mako leaping from the water just a mile from a popular tourist spot.

The 15ft predator – whose name is derived from Maori for 'maneater' – was spotted on Tuesday near Bude.

Alan Britton, 58, was terrified when he saw the shark – a cousin of the great white – leap from the water as he and three friends enjoyed a fishing trip.

"I couldn't beli—" said.

Terrified: Alan Britton

every day that you have a predator like that just feet away.

"I am glad I didn't try to land it.

It was the second mako shark to be spotted off the Cornish coast in just two weeks.

Last month —

near R—

called "mouthing"— basically testing whether you are edible.

"If a swimmer w— there would—

to 60mph—

Western Morning News — SOUTH WEST DAILY

Gig rowers say blue shark swam under their boat 'looking for foo—

● ON THE PROM: The curator at Newquay's Blue Reef Aquarium says blue sharks do not attack people and are normally quite timid

Blue shark spotted in Cornish waters

FAYRE MANN

A BLUE shark has been spotted in waters off the West —

"I caught a blue shark once while I was in waters off the coast of Scilly.

The shark was seen on Wednesday night at around 7pm at the time and about 800 metres off Maenese —

Mr Shaw said there are 27 different types of shark swimming in British waters.

He said: "Most of them are quite small but the blue, porbeagle and mako sharks can grow to be quite large.

"Blue sharks can grow up to 120 and some in the UK up to 250, although they do not often attack humans.

"It was moving the way sharks do when they look for food"

NEWS — newscornwall.co.uk

Thursday, August 18, 2005

The Mako shark: only a total of eight attacks have been reported worldwide.

'This is not Jaws visits Cornwall'

by **IAN SHEPHERD**

WILDLIFE experts and tourism bosses called for calm this week over possible sightings of Mako sharks in Cornish coastal waters.

Western Morning News — SOUTH WEST DAILY NEWSP—

Shark warning as Mako spotted offsh—

DAVID WILCOCK

SWIMMERS in one around Westcountry beaches have been advised to leave the water if they spot sharks, after fishermen made the second sighting of a dangerous Mako shark this year.

● NO CATCH: Alan Britton, who spotted the Mako on a shark fishing trip, said he w—

What to do if you meet creature in the water

The best thing to do if you are in the water off the beach and you spot one of these sharks is to get out of the water or clamber on to your surfboard, a shark expert said yesterday.

90

MARINE EXPERT BELIEVES WESTCOUNTRY'S SEAS

Great whites could

Large sharks have been spotted off the British coast in recent years – and some men claim to have seen great... Rohan ...predatory
THE SUN, Friday, June 16, 2006

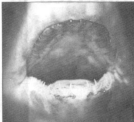

● DEADLY: A fine array of teeth on this porbeagle caught off Cornwall

GREAT WHITES TO STALK UK BEACHES
Killer shark warning

By JOHN GOLES

GREAT White Sharks could soon be swimming near BRITISH holiday beaches because of global warming, an expert warned yesterday.

Marine researcher Anuschka de Rohan said UK waters are fast becoming an ideal feeding ground.

...Great White. Above, scene off Cornwall

● OCCASIONA

'It was big enough to

IN the summer of 2005, Guy Hawkins went spear-fishing for flatfish off Portland Bill. As he descended through the water, something grey swam past him. From its size and shape, he knew immediately that it wasn't a dolphin.

"It came back towards me and stopped just a few inches away," Guy recalls. He got a good look at it and realised it was a shark. Measuring about ...

25-1 ODDS FOR A GREAT WHITE

Bookies set the rate for a killer shark in Westcountry

JAWS: THE BLOODY LEGACY

(or how his creator died, bitterly regretting the book that nearly wiped out the Great White)

lurk in our waters

FEARSOME PREDATOR:
A great white shark

Wildlife

SHARKS
IN THE UK

Rare visitors

IT is unlikely that great whites travel to the UK on a regular basis in the same way that blue sharks do. If they did, we would certainly know about it.

But could the odd great white visit our shores by chance? After all, other big sharks turn up here. For instance, smooth hammerhead sharks migrate north from subtropical waters in summer and some stray into British waters.

EXCLUSIVE: THE CORNISH JAWS

Saturday, July 28, 2007   65p   thesun.co.uk

GREAT WHITE SHARK OFF UK

XCLUSIVE: GREAT

Just when you thought it was safe to go back to Cornwall

Poor publicity and taste for the exotic put sharks on danger list

Hannah Devlin

AT RISK OF EXTINCTION

SOUPFIN SHARK
Length: up to 6ft

ANGEL SHARK
Length: up to 6ft

WHALE SHARK
Length: up to 60ft

BASKING SHARK
Length: up to 50ft

Diver to scale

DOGSHARK
(lifesize)

• Sharks have been on Earth for more than 400 million years, long before the time of the dinosaurs

• Sharks have the most powerful jaws on the planet. Unlike most animals' jaws, both the shark's upper and lower jaws move

• The smallest shark is the 6in dwarf dogshark and the largest is

the whale shark, which can grow to nearly 60ft

• There are about 400 species of sharks and more than 70 in European waters

• Sharks never run out of teeth. If one is lost, another moves forward from the rows of backup teeth

• Not all sharks are fierce carnivores – the enormous basking and whale sharks both live on a diet of plankton

• Sharks are publicised "man-eaters" but people are more likely to be killed by lightning than by shark

Why Jaws may soon be on his way to our shores

By Jo Macfarlane

RISING sea temperatures could mean British beaches being menaced by deadly great white sharks, it was claimed yesterday.

KILLER The deadly great white shark may soon be a threat to bathers and surfers at resorts like St Ives in Cornwall, right

Mauled . . . the seal with huge bite mark
Picture: CHRIS TAYLOR

JAWS ATE SEAL OFF NORFOLK
Hunt on for giant shark

pits nature's greatest predator against caged ce

HAVE WE TURNED SHARKS INTO MAN EATERS?

had their interest in Shark Alley sparked by a recent 'Cumbrian attack' in the part year. Cumbrian fisherman Mark Currie was reported to have been attacked by a Great White while cage-diving there in December 2004.

Mr Currie's experience certainly sounds terrifying. According to his account, after making repeated lunges at the cage, the 20ft creature nearly chewed through the metal bars, severed the connection to a buoy (nearly sending the cage to the abyss) and generally traumatised the hapless tourist.

He did, however, manage to film the encounter and later sold the photographs to a newspaper.

The truth, according to the Shark Trust, is rather more prosaic. The shark — which was considerably smaller than 20ft — simply 'mouthed' the cage (a common occurrence), did not try to bite through the bars and at no time was Mr Currie in any danger.

'The damage done by this story not only to shark eco-tourism but to the image of sharks in general is immense and irresponsible,' Ms Hoult says.

The case of Mr Currie is the latest in a long line of myths surrounding this most enigmatic of creatures.

The Ancient Greeks and Romans were well aware that sharks could attack and devour humans, and in 500BC historian Herodotus described the most impressive predator in the sea.

BUT IN relatively recent times, a new myth took hold: one that said the shark was harmless and posed no threat to humans.

In 1891, Hermann Oelrichs, an American socialite and millionaire, bet $500 to anyone who could prove that sharks attacked humans. To make his point, he took a party of observers out to sea, found a shoal of large sharks, jumped in and swam unharmed with the predators for several minutes.

Then, in 1915, an article appeared in the New York Times written by the director of the American Museum of Natural History, Dr Fredrick Lucas. The article stated the scientific consensus at the time: sharks were timid creatures whose bite was nowhere near strong enough to damage a human.

All that changed in the summer of 1916. Along the Eastern seaboard of the United States, sea-bathing had become popular as the new railways allowed thousands of city dwellers to escape the stifling heat.

But that year, something very large and nasty swam into the inshore waters off the resorts, sowing a panic and fear that has still not abated whenever that triangular fin is spotted in the sea.

Three men and a young boy lost their lives when what is believed to have been a Great White shark left its usual deep water habitat and headed for the beaches. The result was predictable — and ghastly.

'His death was the most horrible thing I ever saw,' said a witness to the end of one Charles Vansant, who had been swimming in just three-and-a-half feet of water when something grabbed him from below.

The water boiled red with blood, and Vansant popped back to the surface, in a bad way. One of his legs had been effectively filleted, stripped of skin, muscle and cartilage down to the bone. He died from blood loss and shock.

After three more deaths and several injuries, the rogue fish now had a price on its head and after a fierce struggle, it was finally killed and found to have 15lb of human flesh in its stomach.

The saga inspired Peter Benchley

to write the novel Jaws, which was later filmed by Steven Spielberg.

Sharks are certainly responsible for some of the most horrible tales of grisly death in history.

When the U.S. cruiser Indianapolis was torpedoed in 1945 off the island of Guam, more than 900 sailors found themselves in the sea.

Over the next five days, a true-life horror story played itself out. The air was rent with the screams of sailors eaten alive by a growing pack of Tiger sharks. More than 400 were eaten.

Whatever their supporters say (including Benchley himself, who regrets having demonised the Great White), sharks are dangerous.

YES, YOU are far more likely to be killed on the drive to the beach than swimming in even the most shark-infested waters.

And yes, if you are a Great White you are millions of times more likely to be killed by a human than the other way round, thanks to the toll taken by tuna fishermen's long lines.

And it is important to realise that sharks are not growing more dangerous, or more common.

Overfishing is probably forcing more sharks to come close to shore in search of prey — increasing the likelihood that they will come into contact with swimmers, as the popularity of watersports and greatly increased tourism to tropical waters sees more people in the sea.

But all that said, there is something so uniquely horrible about the thought of being eaten alive in an alien environment that sharks will probably never lose their terror in the minds of most of us.

In an ever more sanitised world, the possibility — however remote — that we will become a meal for an animal which evolved before the dinosaurs provides an entertaining frisson of fear whenever we take a dip.

Surely we do not need caged 'celebrities' to make one of the most compelling animals ever to have evolved even more exciting than nature intended.

Jaw-dropper .. our man — and cage

By
JEROME STARKEY

THIS is the moment The Sun came face to face with Jaws — off CORNWALL.

We sent trembling reporter Jerome Starkey down in a cage to probe the increasing numbers of sharks drawn to Britain's warmer waters.

He got the shock of his life — as fish scraps thrown in after him lured a potentially deadly Great Blue within **INCHES**.

Jerome, 25 — the first journalist to confront the terrifying creatures off our coast — lived to tell the tale. He shuddered yesterday:

⬤ The Great Blue is known to have killed four — and earned a fearsome reputation for attacking survivors of torpedoed World War II boats.

This one was bigger than me — and hungry. The two metre-long female fixed me with an unblinking eye.

Then suddenly she **ATTACKED**. In a flash of her bright blue flanks and her ghostly white underbelly, she lunged at a bait tube dangling just...

Just as...

and slu...

Shark at...

Sun man goes face to face with killer blue shark off the coast of CORNWALL!

Brave face . . . Sun's Jerome prepares to be lowered into deep

Shark bait . . . trembling Jerome in cage. Picture: COLIN SHEPHERD

CAGE FRIGHT

Stunning

"MY GOD, I CAN'T BELIEVE IT... THERE'S A **TRAIN**!"

Tom Johnston

96

Western Morning News

Thursday June 15 2006

Cornwall's Only Local Daily Newspaper

PRINCE CHARLES VISITS CORNWALL

Full report and pictures– Page 7

WIN A DUNE BUGGY

Full details inside

TOKEN COLLECT

BUSINESS &JOBS

Eight pages of the top vacancies

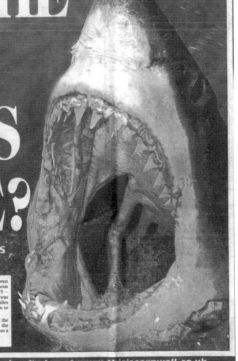

WILL THE GREAT WHITES ARRIVE?

World shark expert predicts killers off our coastline

GREAT white sharks – one of the world's most fearsome predators – could be lurking off the Westcountry coast, according to a wildlife expert.

Anuschka De Rohan, who has just spent a year making a television documentary about great whites for the BBC, claims that the region's bountiful seas, favourable temperatures and proximity to the Mediterranean, where the shark is much more common, make it very possible that the species are in our waters. To date, there have been no proven records of the great whites – made infamous by the Oscar-winning film Jaws in 1975 – visiting our shores, but in 1977, one was caught in the Bay of Biscay, less than 300 miles from Land's End. Great whites are known to roam for thousands of miles.

Ms De Rohan said: "We have some of the most productive fishing grounds on the planet. Great whites eat almost anything, so a visit from one is indeed possible."

■ Full story – Pages 8 & 9

The heart-stopping moment Jaws tried a snack attack on a tourist boat

He's behind you!

Above: Smiling for the camera as the shark takes the tuna
Right: Open wide ... the shark surges up towards the boat

Mail Foreign Service
in Adelaide

WHEN the gigantic shark snapped up the tuna fish that was dangling over the side of the boat, the tourists were delighted.

It was the picture they had wanted – them on deck, the monster in a feeding frenzy in the background.

But seconds later, their smiles for the camera turned to cries of horror ... as the 14ft great white shark finished its lunch and tried to have them for afters.

Mouth agape, it suddenly surged out of the water behind them in a chilling real-life replay of those terrifying scenes from Jaws.

As it came within inches of making a meal of them, one of the tourists, Peter Otto, managed to get this staggering close-up picture of the fish's devilish dental equipment.

The brush with death took place on a shark-watching expedition in the Southern Ocean off Port Lincoln, near Adelaide, South Australia.

Conservationist Andrew Fox organises the trips, in which a baited line is used to attract the creatures, giving tourists a close encounter. But not usually as close as this.

Mr Fox and his father Rodney – who survived a shark attack in 1963 – use the expeditions to fund research on the great whites, which are in decline, partly due to overfishing.

Ironically, for all its terrifying power, the great white seen here looks doomed to become a victim of Man.

Those on the boat noticed it had an old fishing line hooked into its dorsal fin, trailing behind it and covered in seaweed.

It cannot be removed without risk to the researchers and is likely to mean loss of the fin, or death.

'Save our sharks' after haul nets 60

Call for an end to persecution of the shark

20 /News

Colony of vulnerable porbeagle sharks at risk after fisherman lands 60 in single day

A REALITY CHECK ON THE WORLD'S MOST MISUNDERSTOOD CREATURE

Richard Peirce, Chairman of the Shark Trust tells **City Times** that shark attacks are mostly cases of mistaken identity and people are more to be blamed for these attacks than the ferocious looking creatures

SHARK TALE

EXPERT: Above, Richard Peirce, chairman of the Shark Trust, and, right, the picture, probably faked, that started a panic

'The level of hype is nonsense' says Shark Trust chairman

by TRISTAN NICHOLS
Maritime Reporter

A CITY shark conservationist has described his anger at the media attention over a "possible" great white shark sighting off the South West coast.

Said Mr Peirce: "In the last 10 or 11 years I have investigated 80 great white incidents in British waters...only five of these sightings remain credible.

The penny is slowly dropping and sharks are starting to get a fairer hearing and be portrayed accurately in some areas of the media.

Cartoon Chris Wylie.

Chapter Ten

STRANGE AND TRUE

A random compendium of little known shark facts:

- British seas are home to at least 30 shark species.

- A Cornish fish merchant was slightly surprised when, having bought a Porbeagle Shark, he cut it open and found a whole pigeon inside. The pigeon's leg ring enabled its owner to be contacted, and he was amazed when he learnt where his pigeon had landed!

- The most northerly shark attack recorded in British waters occurred in 1960, when a young German sailor off northern Scotland was bitten by a small shark caught in a net.

- A mermaid's purse is an egg case that may well have contained a baby shark.

- The "rock salmon" we see on sale in British fish and chip shops is actually shark – Spiny Dogfish.

- Many of Dublin's street lamps were once fuelled by oil from Basking Sharks' livers.

- In 1961 the Shark Angling Club recorded 6000 Blue Sharks caught off Looe in Cornwall by boats reporting to the club. In 2007, the figure was 142.

- In December 2006 the Angel Shark was declared "locally extinct" in the North Sea by ICES (International Council for the Exploration of the Seas)

- Blue Sharks caught and tagged off Cornwall have more than once been re-caught off the eastern United States.

- In Britain there has only ever been one real recorded shark "attack". Cows are statistically more dangerous to Britons than sharks!

- There is much speculation about how the Porbeagle Shark got its name, and there are many theories. One is that it comes from the Cornish "porth" for harbour and "bugel" meaning shepherd.

- Many sharks "breach" or leap out of the water, including the Great White, Mako, Thresher and Basking Shark. But few people will ever get as close to a shark breaching as Ross Staplehurst and Danny Vokins, when a 181 kilo, 4.5 metre unhooked, free-swimming Thresher Shark jumped into their 6.7 metre (22 foot) boat off the Isle of Wight in June 1981

- At Mr Kai's restaurant in London's Mayfair in 2006, bowls of sharks fin soup were on the menu at a cost of £108 each

- The Mako is said to be the fastest shark. Swim speed estimates vary from 20mph to 50 mph.

- In 1977, a Japanese trawler pulled up the decayed remains of a Basking Shark, which was mistaken for a sea monster (a plesiosaur). Basking Sharks are known to decompose into "pseudoplesiosaur" forms and their carcasses have often been mistaken for sea monsters.

- Tagging has established that Soupfin Sharks (Tope) can live for more than 50 years.

- Basking Sharks may well filter more than 1800 cubic metres of water an hour. That is roughly the equivalent of an Olympic swimming pool.

- In 1986 a research team went to the Canary Islands to find out what had been biting fibre optic cables between Tenerife and Gran Canaria. The culprit turned out to be none other than the Kitefin shark, a species also found in British waters.

- From "Shark Attack" by H. David Baldridge. "In reply to a question concerning the Royal Navy's wartime need for an effective shark repellent, Prime Minister Winston Churchill assured the House of Commons that "...the British Government is entirely opposed to sharks".

- The Greenland Shark is the only shark to live in the Arctic Sea and reputedly lures prey fish by using white, possibly luminous, parasitic copepods attached to its eyes.

- As far as I have been able to determine the only British shark related deaths occurred in 1937 off Port Righ to the north of Carradale on the Kintyre Peninsula. Captain Angus Brown, his daughter, Jessica, his son, Neil, his brother, Robert, and a friend, Donald MacDonald, were all aboard a 4.6 metre (15 foot) clinker built sailing/rowing dinghy that was capsized by a Basking Shark breaching. Captain Brown, his son and his brother all drowned, while Jessica and Donald MacDonald survived.

- Alex McCormack's book "Shark Attack" relates four out of the water shark attacks in England as follows!

- Darren Smith, a chef from Newquay was driving to a restaurant with a 2.15 metre Porbeagle Shark in an icebox in his vehicle. He braked sharply and the 50 kilo shark shot forward. When he tried to push it back he caught his hand in its mouth and severed an artery needing 17 stitches.

- In December 2000 The Sun reported that Paul Smith, a chef working at the Fountain in Tenbury Wells, Worcester, was attacked by Black Tip Reef Shark in a 4.6 metre x 1.5m metre tank in the pub as he fed them prawns. The landlord, Russell Allen, took Smith to hospital, where he needed six stitches.

- The landlady of the Wheatsheaf at Boughbeech, near Edenbridge, in Kent, was badly cut when a stuffed shark hanging on the wall fell off and injured her.

- In April 1995 the People reported that a mother and her three children were treated by ambulancemen having inhaled fumes from a dead shark. It had been kept in formaldehyde and other toxic preservatives and left at their home.

- Most of us would want a shark attack about as much as we would want a hole in the head. Skipper Phil Hambridge, of Sabre Tooth II based in Neyland Marina, Pembrokeshire, got both. He hooked a 45 kilo Blue Shark that had another hook lightly caught in its tail. There was an energetic flick of the tail and the hook flew through the air and embedded itself in Phil's head. He had to be helicopter evacuated to hospital for the hook to be removed.

- Male Blue Sharks are very aggressive during mating and grip the females with their teeth during the process. However, female Blue Sharks have skin two-to-three times the thickness of males to give them some protection during these amorous encounters.

- Legend has it that Blue Sharks will follow a ship on which someone has died waiting for the body to be committed to the sea.

- In 1989 fifty-seven Basking Sharks swam into Peel harbour on the Isle of Man. It was one of three large schools that came close inshore on the west side of the island that year.

- The Cookiecutter * or Cigar Shark swallows its teeth. It is thought it does this to extract the calcium.

- Sandtiger * Shark pups are cannibals before they are born. Pups not only eat infertile eggs while still in the uterus but also eat other developing pups.

- Tiger * Sharks give a new meaning to being omnivorous. Car licence plates, a chair leg, human body parts, birds and turtles are among the many items found in their stomachs.

* THESE SHARKS ARE NOT FOUND IN BRITISH SEAS.

This humerous cartoon has a serious message which is that 70-100 million sharks are killed globally each year to fuel the trade which supplies shark fins for soup. Cartoon Chris Wylie.

Chapter Eleven

SHARK FISHERIES & THE CONSERVATION & FUTURE OF OUR SHARKS

Few creatures on land or sea have been as unsustainably and often cruelly exploited as sharks. All the large species found in our waters are seriously depleted and many of our smaller sharks are also listed as threatened or critically endangered.

Research carried out by the Dalhousie University in Nova Scotia, Canada, has produced figures based on 15 years of catch reports from the western Atlantic. Regrettably, there is no similar research for the eastern side of the Atlantic. However, it is reasonable to assume that for some species the position is similar and, for others, virtually the same. The Blue Shark, for example, is involved in a continual circular migration around the north Atlantic and is one population, and so the western Atlantic figures will probably apply to the eastern side.

Fishing pressures on sharks have not slackened since the research was published so the depletion rates today are likely to be even higher. Figures relevant to some species found in British waters are as follows:

Blue Shark - depleted by 60 per cent
Shortfin Mako - moderate decline
Thresher Shark - depleted by 80 per cent
Hammerhead Shark - depleted by 89 per cent

Different species are caught for different reasons, but the single most important reason that most large sharks are caught is for their fins. As the economies of China and other Far Eastern nations have developed, shark fin soup has become an affordable luxury for an ever-increasing market. And, shamefully, the European Union is one of the largest suppliers of fins to those markets. Spanish fishing fleets

Porbeagles in crates in Newlyn market awaiting sale. © Jed Trewin

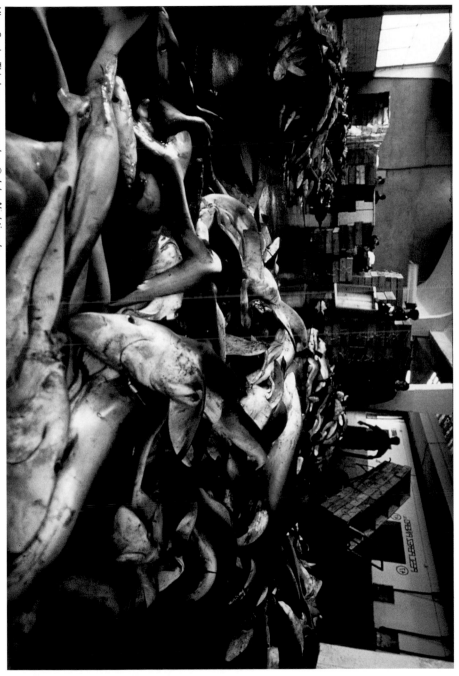

Vigo, Spain. This happens everyday. © John Nightingale

harvest enormous numbers of sharks and supplied about 11 per cent of the total Hong Kong fin market in 2005. The number of fins supplied by Great Britain is thought to be negligible.

The high value of fins has meant that sharks have ceased to be nuisance by-catch, which, if put back, would have a chance of survival. Instead, they have become a highly valuable targeted catch. Longline fishing boats traditionally targeted tuna, swordfish, marlin, and others. Lines of more than 20 kilometres are usual with baited hooks every two to three metres. The deployment of just one line can catch hundreds of sharks. To ease storage and transportation problems and avoid taking the time required to kill the shark (as well as not having the risk of shark flesh tainting other fish), the sharks are often finned and thrown back into the ocean while still alive, to die a slow and painful death.

The Porbeagle Shark is very vulnerable to over fishing due to its tendency to aggregate (form groups). This makes it easy prey for longliners. Two recent cases of large Porbeagle catches by longliners in the UK were in 2003, when one longliner was reported to have taken more than 130 sharks off south Cornwall, and in August 2007, when another took between 60 and 90 sharks near Lundy Island in the Bristol Channel.

In 2005, a Lowestoft-based company was planning a specific trade in Soupfin Sharks. Like Porbeagles, Soupfin Sharks (Tope) have a tendency to school that makes them vulnerable to over fishing. However, the venture was shelved, partly due to the efforts of various activist groups, and partly for economic reasons.

All of the species mentioned in this book as British sharks appear on the IUCN Red List of Threatened Species. (See the following table):

IUCN Red List Status of British Sharks Species
(Source – International Union for the Consevatioon of Nature, Shark Specialist Group).

Species	IUCN Red List Category		
	*NEA** *	*Global*	*Year*
Angelshark		Critically Endangered	2006
Spiny Dogfish (Spurdog)	Critically Endangered	Vulnerable	2006
Porbeagle Shark	Critically Endangered	Vulnerable	2005
Portuguese Dogfish	Endangered	Vulnerable	2008*
Leafscale Gulper Shark	Endangered	Vulnerable	2008*
Basking Shark	Endangered	Vulnerable	2000
Thresher Shark		Vulnerable	2008*
Shortfin Mako		Vulnerable	2008*
Angular Roughshark		Vulnerable	2007
Soupfin Shark (Tope)		Vulnerable	2005
Nursehound		Near Threatened	2008*
Sharpnose Sevengill Shark		Near Threatened	2007

	NEA**	Global	Year
Bluntnose Sixgill Shark		Near Threatened	2003
Frilled Shark		Near Threatened	2003
Blue Shark		Near Threatened	2000
Smooth Hammerhead		Near Threatened	2000
Black Dogfish	Near Threatened	Least Concern	2008*
Velvet Belly	Near Threatened	Least Concern	2005
Greenland Shark	Near Threatened	Least Concern	2005
Blackmouth Catshark		Least Concern	2008*
Smallspotted Catshark		Least Concern	2008*
Ghost Catshark		Least Concern	2004
Birdbeak Dogfish		Least Concern	2003
Longnose Velvet Dogfish		Least Concern	2003
Starry Smoothhound		Least Concern	2000
Smoothhound		Least Concern	2000
Great Lanternshark		Data Deficient	2008*
Knifetooth Dogfish		Data Deficient	2008*
Sailfin Roughshark		Data Deficient	2008*
Iceland Shark		Data Deficient	2007
Velvet Dogfish		Data Deficient	2005
Whiteghost Catshark		Data Deficient	2004
Bramble Shark		Data Deficient	2003
Kitefin Shark		Data Deficient	2000

(*Data "in preparation" at the time of going to press, ** North East Atlantic).

In total, 30 per cent of British sharks are considered threatened. Of these, 9 per cent (three species) are "Critically Endangered", 9 per cent (three species) are "Endangered" and 12 per cent (four species) are "Vulnerable". A further 26 per cent (nine species) are considered "Near Threatened". Only seven species (21 per cent) are considered to be of Least Concern, and, currently, too little is known about eight species (23 per cent) to be able to assess them beyond "Data Deficient". These species will be re-assessed as soon as more information becomes available.

While many of the deepwater sharks on the list are categorised "Data deficient", scientists know enough about their life histories to recognise the urgent need for their protection. Deepwater sharks such as the Portuguese Dogfish and the Leafscale Gulper Shark have been targeted by a gill net fishery off north west Scotland, and have had their populations reduced by over 80 per cent. Their liver oil (squalene) and meat (siki) are valuable products that have made the trade worthwhile. The fishery is now closed to gill nets, but is still open to deepwater trawls and longlining, and the damage to shark populations will take decades to repair. It is thought likely that the Leafscale Gulper Shark has a particularly long two-year gestation period and produces only five to eight pups per pregnancy, so perhaps decades is optimistic! With such a low reproductive capability recovery may actually take hundreds of years.

As mentioned previously in Chapter 6 sustained over fishing of Angel Sharks and Spurdogs (Spiny Dogfish) has pushed both populations to the edge of collapse in British waters. Indeed the Angel Shark was declared extinct in the North Sea in 2006. The Basking Shark now enjoys protection but was once taken in enormous numbers (see Chapter 4). This species was actively hunted until the 1990's, and despite being protected in European waters, two Basking Sharks were landed in Belgium in 2007 and ended up being offered for sale in Bruges market. In March 2008 the Angel Shark received long awaited protection in English waters out to six miles under the Wildlife and Countryside Act. However protection in Scottish, Welsh and Northern Irish waters has yet to be achieved. Conservationists believe the management measures in place for the Spurdog are inadequate and need addressing. The Porbeagle recieved some management under the new 2007 TAC (Total Allowable Catch) negotiations but conservationists felt the figures agreed for some European countries were too high.

I have often heard it said that the only good shark is a dead shark, and have been asked why we need sharks. Wouldn't we be better off if this "dangerous-to-man" predator disappeared altogether?

My answers are as follows:

- The moral argument. In Britain we pride ourselves on fairness. The annual killing by hunting of up to 19,000 foxes provoked a fierce debate that rumbled on for years. Yet the fact that between 70 and 100 million sharks have been taken annually by unsustainable fisheries and pushed towards extinction has started to be a concern only recently. It cannot be morally right that one of earth's newest arrivals (mankind) should be systematically wiping out a whole group of species that are among the oldest inhabitants of our planet.

- Self interest. Life on earth as we know it needs healthy oceans to survive. Oceans stay healthy only if marine eco-systems remain in balance. Science has shown that the removal of the apex predator from ocean food chains causes modification and, sometimes, the collapse of marine eco-systems. Self- interest should dictate that man recognises that sick seas could herald an uninhabitable planet. Sharks and other apex marine predators are a major part of this equation.

- The emotional argument. To me, sharks are one of the most beautiful animals on earth. They are also relatively harmless compared with many other sea and land creatures that are responsible for far more human deaths. How can we destroy these beautiful creatures largely for the sake of boring, bland-tasting bowls of soup? The television presenter Monty Halls likens the wiping out of sharks to the wholesale slaughter of the North American plains bison. Plains, which were home to teeming herds of millions of buffalo, are now empty. In parts of the North Atlantic the ocean is now missing between 80 to 90 per cent of those sharks that were there 50 years ago.

- Economic benefit. In several countries sharks are producing large revenues for eco-tourist operators and, thereby, supporting local businesses. A dead shark is "one time usage", whereas shark catch-and-release, and shark watching are repeat multi-usages, which generate a great deal more money. My view is that the only way wildlife will survive co-existing with man is by paying its way. Sharks can be long-term earners, and this alone is a powerful argument for their future.

Sharks mature late, have long gestation periods and then produce only a few young. The time for British and European legislators to act effectively is long over-due. Let's hope they don't leave it until it becomes too late, and more species join the Angel Shark on local extinction lists.

The bad image sharks have due to their occasional attacks on man doesn't help them gain human supporters, nor does their being classified as fish. Fish are part of our diet and come under fisheries management policies. Wildlife is regarded differently, and were sharks deemed to be wildlife rather than fish, they would probably get considerably more effective protection. As it happens, the life cycles of sharks are closer to those of mammals than fish – and mammals are wildlife.

The Shark Trust in the UK spearheads campaigns aimed at raising public awareness of the vulnerability of sharks. It is also involved in lobbying EU and UK government agencies to ensure effective action against shark finning, sustainable fisheries policies, and other shark management measures. In addition to the Shark Trust, the World Wildlife Fund, the Marine Conservation Society, the International Fund for Animal Welfare, the Shark Alliance, Bite Back, Greenpeace, Sea Shepherd, the Wildlife Trusts, IUCN (SSG), various angling groups, and statutory agencies are all active in a variety of shark conservation strategies.

So, now, an unashamed plug! At the time of writing, I am Chairman of the Shark Trust and if, in this book, I have managed to interest you in sharks, and to make you worry about their future then please visit the Trust's website www.sharktrust.org and consider becoming a registered supporter.

Becoming a Shark Trust supporter is one way you can help ensure these beautiful and wonderful creatures continue to exist for future generations on a healthy planet.

THE SHARK DIRECTORY

RESIDENT/REGULAR VISITORS

Angel Shark
Basking Shark
Blue Shark
Greenland Shark
Nursehound Shark
Porbeagle Shark
Bluntnose Sixgill Shark
Sharpnose Sevengill Shark
Shortfin Mako Shark
Smallspotted Catshark
Smoothhound Shark
Starry Smoothhound Shark
Soupfin Shark (Tope)
Spurdog Shark (Spiny Dogfish)
Thresher Shark

RARE/DEEPWATER

Angular Roughshark
Sailfin Roughshark

Birdbeak Dogfish
Leafscale Gulper Shark

Black Dogfish
Great Lantern Shark
Velvet Belly Shark

Bramble Shark

Blackmouth Catshark

Frilled Shark

Ghost Catshark
Iceland Catshark
Whiteghost Catshark

Kitefin Shark

Longnose Velvet Dogfish
Knifetooth Dogfish
Velvet Dogfish

Portuguese Dogfish

Smooth Hammerhead

CLASSIFICATION OF SHARKS

Sharks are divided into eight major groups or orders.

Hexanchiformes - Six or seven gill slits, one dorsal fin.
Squaliformes - Five gill slits, two dorsal fins, short snout.
Pristiophoriformes - Five or six gill slits, two dorsal fins, snout long and saw-like.
Squatiniformes - Five gill slits, two dorsal fins, long and saw-like snout, flattened body.
Heterodontiformes - Five gill slits, two dorsal fins, dorsal fin spines.
Orectolobiformes - Five gill slits, two dorsal fins, mouth well in front of eyes.
Lamniformes - Five gill slits, two dorsal fins, no nictating eyelid.
Carcharhiniformes - Nictating eyelid, five gill slits, two dorsal fins.

REPRODUCTION

More than 450 different sharks in eight orders reproduce in different ways.

• Oviparity. This describes egg laying. These hatch externally and about forty per cent of sharks are born this way. After fertilisation, each egg is enclosed in a tough, flexible case known to many as a mermaid's purse. This method applies to Catsharks, Epaulette Sharks, Horn sharks and others.

• Ovoviviparity. This involves the females retaining the eggs. They then absorb the yolk, the young animal develops and hatches inside the mother and is born fully developed. About 25 per cent of sharks reproduce this way including Whale Sharks, and the Spiny Dogfish which is a resident in British seas.

• Oophagy. Some members of the lamnid family produce large numbers of infertile eggs and only one fertile egg in each ovary. The infertile eggs are eaten by the young in uteri. Sandtiger Sharks (not a British species) go one stage further with pups in the uterus not only eating infertile eggs but also each other.

• Placental viviparity. This method is closest to that of most mammals and involves a placenta and an umbilical cord providing a link between the mother and the embryo. This is the most advanced method of reproduction found in sharks and applies to around 10 per cent of species.

RESIDENTS AND REGULAR VISITORS

ANGEL SHARK
(Squatina squatina)

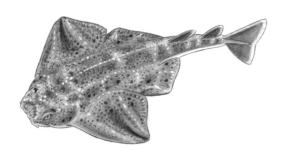

Size:	Maximum 2.4 metres (7ft 8 ins)
Identification:	Large and squat. Reddish-grey brown back with dots and spots.
Distribution:	N.E. Atlantic, Mediterranean, Black Sea.
Habitat:	Inshore down to 150 metres. Mostly on the bottom.
Diet/Behaviour:	Skates, flatfish, molluscs, crustaceans. Rests by day, hunts by night.
Biology:	Ovoviviparous. Up to 25 pups a litter.

BASKING SHARK
(Cetorhinus maximus)

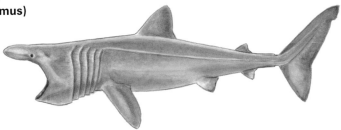

Size:	Maximum 10 metres (32/33 ft)
Identification:	Grey to bronzy brown, often mottled. Lighter below.
Distribution:	Worldwide in temperate seas.
Habitat:	Coast to continental shelf edge.
Diet/Behaviour:	Plankton feeder. Highly migratory. Often seen breaching.
Biology:	Probably oophagy. A litter of 6 pups reported.

BLUE SHARK
(Prionace glauca)

Size:	Maximum 3.8 metres (12 ft 5 ins)
Identification:	Blue back, lighter blue sides, white below. Slim shark, long snout.
Distribution:	Worldwide in temperate and tropical waters.
Habitat:	Migratory, pelagic & oceanic. Rarely found close inshore.
Diet/Behaviour:	Squid, pelagic fish, small sharks, invertebrates, sea birds. Listed as being potentially dangerous to man.
Biology:	Viviparous. Up to 140 pups a litter.

GREENLAND SHARK
(Somniosus microcephalus)

Size:	Maximum 7 metres (22 ft 9 ins)
Identification:	Very large shark, heavy body. Grey brown colour.
Distribution:	North Atlantic and Arctic.
Habitat:	Continental and insular shelves to 1200 metres.
Diet/Behaviour:	Fishes, invertebrates, seals, seabirds and scavenges. Slow moving.
Biology:	Ovoviviparous up to 10 pups a litter.

NURSEHOUND SHARK
(Scyliorhinus stellaris)

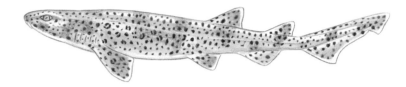

Size: Maximum 1.6 metres (5ft 4 ins)
Identification: Pale golden brown background with black spots.
Distribution: Northeast Atlantic and Mediterranean.
Habitat: Continental and insular shelves to 100 metres.
Diet/Behaviour: Eats crustaceans. Does well in captivity.
Biology: Ovoviviparous. Up to 15 pups a litter.

PORBEAGLE SHARK
(Lamna nasus)

Size: Maximum 3 metres (9 – 10 ft)
Identification: Stout stocky shark. Distinctive white marking on rear of front
                 dorsal fin.
Distribution: Temperate and cool seas, northern and southern hemispheres.
Habitat: Inshore to open ocean.
Diet/Behaviour: Small fishes, small sharks, squid. Migratory and will school.
Biology: Ovoviviparous/oophagy/normally 4 or 5 pups a litter.

BLUNTNOSE SIXGILL SHARK
(Hexanchus griseus)

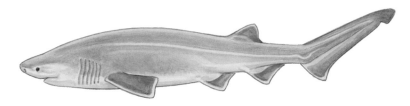

Size: Maximum 4.82 metres (15 ft 8 ins)
Identification: Large shark with broad head and wide mouth.
                   Grey to black with a light coloured lateral line.
Distribution: Worldwide except probably not in the Arctic and Antarctic.
Habitat: Shelves and slopes of continents, mid ocean ridges
                   and islands.
Diet/Behaviour: Squid, pelagic bony fishes, small sharks and rays. Large
                   specimens may take small cetaceans and seals. Slow strong
                   swimming shark generally observed as being docile except
                   when captured or in baited situations.
Biology: Ovoviviparous, large litters of up to 100 pups.

SHARPNOSE SEVENGILL SHARK
(Heptranchias perlo)

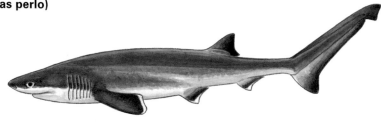

Size: Maximum 1.4 metres (4 ft 6 ins)
Identification: Seven pairs of gill slits, pointed head, narrow mouth
                   with large eyes.
Distribution: Worldwide throughout tropical and temperate seas except the
                   Northeast Pacific.
Habitat: Occasionally shallow but mostly deepwater
Diet/Behaviour: Small sharks, squid, pelagic fishes, and crustaceans. Strong
                   swimmer, little known about behaviour.
Biology: Ovoviviparous, up to 20 pups per litter.

SHORTFIN MAKO SHARK
(Isurus oxyrinchus)

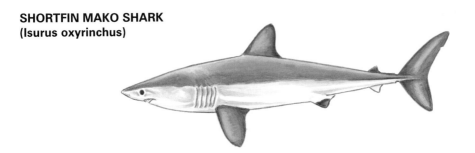

Size:	Maximum 4 metres (13 ft)
Identification:	Blue, purple to black topside, light (whitish) below.
Distribution:	Worldwide in temperate and tropical seas.
Habitat:	Oceanic and coastal. Surface down to 500 – 600 metres.
Diet/Behaviour:	Fishes, squid, smaller sharks may be small cetaceans. Said to be the fastest shark in the world.
Biology:	Ovoviviparous, up to 25 pups a litter.

SMALLSPOTTED CATSHARK
(Scyliorhinus canicula)

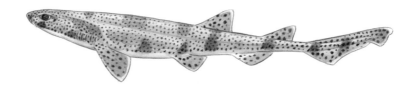

Size:	Maximum 0.45 metres (18 inches)
Identification:	Slender, dark spots on light background.
Distribution:	Northeast Atlantic, North Sea, Mediterranean.
Habitat:	Continental shelves.
Diet/Behaviour:	Small crustaceans, gastropods, cephalopods, fishes. Young often in shallower water.
Biology:	Oviparous.

SMOOTHHOUND SHARK
(Mustelus mustelus)

Size: Maximum 1.64 metres (5 ft 4 ins)
Identification: Fairly slender. Grey to grey brown above, lighter below,
                   short snout.
Distribution: Temperate, Mediterranean & northeast Atlantic.
                   May be also in south Atlantic.
Habitat: Continental shelves and upper slopes, surface down to
                   50 metres.
Diet/Behaviour: Feeds primarily on crustaceans but also on bony fishes
                   and cephalopods.
Biology: Viviparous. Up to 15 pups a litter.

STARRY SMOOTHHOUND SHARK
(Mustelus asterias)

Size: Maximum 1.4 metres (4 ft 7 ins)
Identification: Small white spots (stars) on grey brown above, lighter below.
Distribution: Northeast Atlantic and Mediterranean.
Habitat: Continental and insular shelves to 100 metres.
Diet/Behaviour: Eats crustaceans. Does well in captivity.
Biology: Ovoviviparous. Up to 15 pups a litter.

SOUPFIN SHARK (TOPE)
(Galeorhinus galeus)

Size:	Maximum 1.64 metres (5 ft 4 ins)
Identification:	Fairly slender. Grey to grey brown above, lighter below, short snout.
Distribution:	Temperate, Mediterranean & northeast Atlantic. Maybe also in South Atlantic.
Habitat:	Continental and insular shelves to 100 metres.
Diet/Behaviour:	Eats bony fishes and invertebrates. Often forms schools.
Biology:	Ovoviviparous. Up to 50 pups a litter.

SPURDOG SHARK (SPINY DOGFISH)
(Squalus acanthias)

Size:	Maximum 2.0 metres (6 ft 5 ins)
Identification:	Blue grey above, lighter below, sometimes with white spots on sides.
Distribution:	Worldwide except poles and tropics.
Habitat:	From surface to bottom, continental and insular shelves.
Diet/Behaviour:	Smaller sharks and rays, bony fishes, invertebrates.
Biology:	Ovoviviparous, litters up to 30 pups.

THRESHER SHARK
(Alopias vulpinus)

Size: Maximum 6.10 metres (19 ft 9 ins)
Identification: Blue to dark grey above, white below.
Distribution: Worldwide, temperate and tropical seas.
Habitat: Surface down to 366 metres. Inshore to mid ocean.
Diet/Behaviour: Bony fishes, squid, small sharks. Known to breach and to hunt
                 co-operatively.
Biology: Ovoviviparous up to 6 pups a litter.

RARE AND DEEPWATER SPECIES

ANGULAR ROUGHSHARK
(Oxynotus centrina)

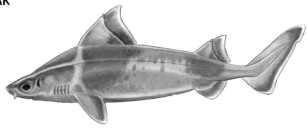

Size:	Maximum 1.5 metres (4 ft 9 ins)
Identification:	Greyish brown to grey with darker patches.
Distribution:	Eastern Atlantic and Mediterranean.
Habitat:	Mostly below 100 metres down to 600 metres. Continental shelves.
Diet/Behaviour:	Eats worms, molluscs and crustaceans. Little known of behaviour.
Biology:	Litters between 7 and 23 pups.

SAILFIN ROUGHSHARK
(Oxynotus paradoxus)

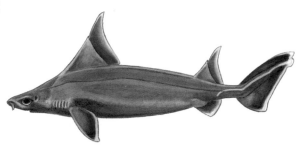

Size:	Maximum 1.18 metres (3 ft 9 ins)
Identification:	Dark brown/black. Two tall dorsal fins.
Distribution:	Northeast Atlantic.
Habitat:	Continental slope. Deepwater down to 720 metres.
Diet/Behaviour:	Little known.
Biology:	Ovoviviparous.

BIRDBEAK DOGFISH
(Deania calcea)

Size: Maximum 1.22 metres (4 ft)
Identification: Grey to dark brown, lighter underneath. Very long flat snout.
Distribution: East Atlantic, Australia, Peru to Chile, New Zealand, Japan.
Habitat: Deepwater. Continental and insular shelves down to
                 1500 metres.
Diet/Behaviour: Bony fishes and shrimps. Sometimes schools.
Biology: Ovoviviparous. Up to twelve pups per litter.

LEAFSCALE GULPER SHARK
(Centrophorus squamosus)

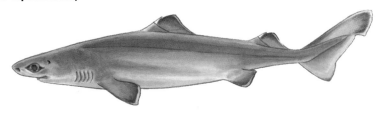

Size: Maximum 1.6 metres (5 ft 3 ins)
Identification: Grey brown or reddish brown. Rough skin, flattened snout.
Distribution: Atlantic and west Pacific and Indian oceans.
Habitat: Deepwater up to 4000 metres.
Diet/Behaviour: Little known.
Biology: Ovoviviparous, up to eight pups per litter.

BLACK DOGFISH
(Centroscyllium fabricii)

Size:	Maximum 1.08 metres (3 ft 5 ins)
Identification:	Browny black all over. Large eyes.
Distribution:	Temperate Atlantic.
Habitat:	Outer continental shelves. Deepwater down to 2000 metres.
Diet/Behaviour:	Eats bony fishes, cephalopods and crustaceans. Known to school.
Biology:	Ovoviviparous. Up to eight pups a litter.

GREAT LANTERN SHARK
(Etmopterus princeps)

Size:	Maximum 75 centimetres (2 ft 5 ins)
Identification:	Dark brown/black all over.
Distribution:	Northwest northeast Atlantic. Maybe in south Atlantic & west Pacific.
Habitat:	Deepwater. Continental slopes down to 4500 metres.
Diet/Behaviour:	Little known.
Biology:	Maybe ovoviviparous.

VELVET BELLY SHARK
(Etmopterus spinax)

Size:	Maximum 60 centimetres (2 ft)
Identification:	Brownish above, black underneath. Very short gill openings.
Distribution:	East Atlantic, Mediterranean.
Habitat:	Mostly 200-500 metres.
Diet/Behaviour:	Eats small fish, squid, crustaceans.
Biology:	Ovoviviparous up to 20 pups a litter.

BRAMBLE SHARK
(Echinorhinus brucus)

Size:	Maximum 3.10 metres (10 ft)
Identification:	Light brown/dark brown with black/red spots on back and sides.
Distribution:	Mainly east Atlantic and Mediterranean.
Habitat:	Continental and Island shelves, deepwater on or near bottom.
Diet/Behaviour:	Small sharks, crustaceans and bony fishes. Behaviour little known.
Biology:	Ovoviviparous, probably up to 30 pups per litter

BLACKMOUTH CATSHARK
(Galeus melastomus)

Size:	Maximum 0.90 metres (3 ft)
Identification:	Distinctive circular spots and blotches, darker brown on lighter background.
Distribution:	Northeast Atlantic, Mediterranean.
Habitat:	Outer continental shelves down to 1000 metres.
Diet/Behaviour:	Bottom invertebrates and lantern fish.
Biology:	Oviparous up to 13 eggs.

FRILLED SHARK
(Chlamydoselachus anguineus)

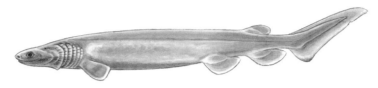

Size:	Maximum 196 cm (6 ft 5 ins)
Identification:	Dark brown/brownish black. Eel/snake shaped with flat snakelike head.
Distribution:	Usually deepwater, worldwide, rare.
Habitat:	Mostly deepwater, very occasionally at the surface.
Diet/Behaviour:	Squid and deepwater fish.
Biology:	Ovoviviparous, 6/12 pups per litter.

GHOST CATSHARK
(Apristurus manis)

Size:	Maximum 0.85 metres (2 ft 9 ins)
Identification:	Dark grey to black. Broad nostrils, flat head.
Distribution:	Northwest Atlantic, north and southeast Atlantic.
Habitat:	Continental slopes down to 1700 metres.
Diet/Behaviour:	Little known.
Biology:	Little known.

ICELAND CATSHARK
(Apristurus laurussoni)

Size: Maximum 0.67 metres (2 ft 2 ins)
Identification: Dark brown. Broad flat head, short snout.
Distribution: Northwest and Northeast Atlantic
Habitat: Deepwater down to 2000 metres.
Diet/Behaviour: Little known.
Biology: Little known.

WHITEGHOST CATSHARK
(Apristurus aphyodes)

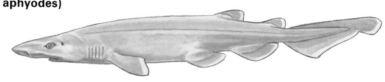

Size: Maximum 0.54 metres (1 ft 9 ins)
Identification: Pale whitish grey. Elongated snout.
Distribution: Northwest Atlantic
Habitat: Deepwater down to 2000 metres
Diet/Behaviour: Little known.
Biology: Little known.

KITEFIN SHARK
(Dalatias licha)

Size: Maximum 1.82 metres (5 ft 9 ins)
Identification: Blackish brown all over. Blunt short snout.
Distribution: Indian, Pacific and Atlantic oceans.
Habitat: Deepwater to 1800 metres.
Diet/Behaviour: Deepwater fishes. Lone hunter.
Biology: Ovoviviparous. Up to 16 pups a litter.

LONGNOSE VELVET DOGFISH
(Centroselachus crepidater)

Size:	Maximum 1.05 metres (3 ft 5 ins)
Identification:	Long snout. Slender and brown to black in colour.
Distribution:	East Atlantic, Indian – Pacific.
Habitat:	Mostly 500 metres. Down to 2000 metres.
Diet/Behaviour:	Fish and cephalopods.
Biology:	Ovoviviparous, up to 8 pups a litter.

KNIFETOOTH DOGFISH
(Scymnodon ringens)

Size:	Maximum 1.10 metres (3 ft 7 ins)
Identification:	Black all over. Short snout.
Distribution:	East Atlantic.
Habitat:	Deepwater. 200 – 1600 metres.
Diet/Behaviour:	Little known.
Biology:	Probably ovoviviparous.

VELVET DOGFISH
(Zameus squamulosus)

Size:	Maximum 0.69 metres (2 ft 4 ins)
Identification:	Black all over. Flat head, long narrow snout.
Distribution:	Patchy worldwide except eastern Pacific.
Habitat:	Deepwater 500 – 1500 metres, continental and insular shelves.
Diet/Behaviour:	Little known.
Biology:	Probably ovoviviparous.

PORTUGUESE DOGFISH
(Centroscymnus coelolepis)

Size:	Maximum 1.2 metres (3 ft 10 ins)
Identification:	Black to golden brown. Short snout.
Distribution:	Atlantic, Indian and Pacific oceans.
Habitat:	On or near bottom, mostly 400-500 metres.
Diet/Behaviour:	Other sharks, bony fishes, cetaceans.
Biology:	Ovoviviparous up to 17 pups per litter.

SMOOTH HAMMERHEAD
(Sphyrna zygaena)

Size:	Maximum 4.0 metres (13 ft)
Identification:	Dark greyish brown above, white below. Large hammerhead.
Distribution:	Worldwide in temperate and tropical waters.
Habitat:	Continental & insular shelves. Mostly near surface.
Diet/Behaviour:	Bony fishes, small sharks, skates & rays.
	Often forms large schools.
Biology:	Viviparous. 30-40 pups per litter.

USEFUL WEBSITES

American Elasmobranch Society	– www.elasmo.org
ElasmoFrance	– www.fredshark.net
Elasmo.com	– www.elasmo.com
Fishbase	– www.fishbase.org
International Shark Attack File	– www.flmnh.ufl.edu/fish/ISAF/ISAF.htm
Italian Research Group	– http://digilander.libero.it/infogris/
Mediterranean Shark Site	– www.zoo.co.uk/-z9015043
Reef Quest Centre for Shark Research	– www.elasmo-research.org
Richard Peirce Shark Conservation	– www.peirceshark.com
Shark Conservation Society	– www.peirceshark.com
Shark Cornwall	– www.peirceshark.com
Shark Research Institute	– www.sharks.org
Shark Trust	– www.sharktrust.org

THANKS AND ACKNOWLEDGEMENTS

I would like to thank the following either for having provided source material or for their direct personal contribution.

Jane Attwood
Rob Allen
Thomas B Allen – *author – The Shark Almanac*
Brian Bates
Chris Bennett – *Porbeagle world record holder (angling)*
Peter Benchley – *author – various*
Karl Bennett – *Skipper - Mantis*
Tony Bennett
Mark Boothman
John Boyle
Michael Bright – *author – Private lives of Sharks*
Phill Britts – Skipper – *Blue Fox*
Anthony Bush/Tim Davison – *Editors*
June Bush – *Typing edited manuscripts*
Brigadier J.A.L. Caunter *(Deceased)* – *author – Shark Angling at Looe*
Mark Cawardine/Ken Watterson – *authors – Shark Watchers Handbook*
Collins – *Sharks of the World*
Tim Davison
Chris Fallows
Teresa Farino – *authoress - Sharks*
Ian Fergusson
Sarah Fowler
Claudine Gibson (IUCN (SSG)
Richard E. Grant
Dr. Simon Greenstreet
Monty Halls
Philip Harding
Denise Headon – *secretary – worn out typing fingers*
Tim Higham
Ali Hood – *The Shark Trust*

Trevor Housby – *author – Shark Fishing in British Waters*
Miranda Krestovnikoff
Richard Lock
Alex MacCormick – *author – Shark Attack*
Marine Conservation Society
Gavin Maxwell – *author – Harpoon at a Venture*
Mac McDiarmid – *author – Shark Attack*
David Mellor
Stuart Nicholls
John Nightingale
Stuart Patterson
Jacqueline Peirce – *wife – incalculable support*
Tony Pimm
Readers Digest – *Sharks*
John Reynolds – *skipper*
Linda Reynolds
Simon Rogerson
Shark Angling Club of Great Britain
Sally Sharrock
Simon Spear
Colin Speedie
Jeremy Stafford-Deitsch
Darren Steadwood
The Shark Trust
Jed Trewin
Paul Vincent
Danny Vokins
Jim Watson
Ken Watterson
Chris Wylie – *Cartoonist*
        and anyone I have forgotten.